ESSENTIAL SKILLS IN
MATHS
Answer Book

BOOK 3

Nelson

Graham Newman and Ron Bull

National Curriculum coverage

Book	1	2	3	4	5
Levels	3–4	4–5	5–6	6–7	7–8

Thomas Nelson and Sons Ltd
Nelson House   Mayfield Road
Walton-on-Thames   Surrey
KT12 5PL   UK

© R. Bull, G. Newman 1996

First published by Thomas Nelson and Sons Ltd 1996

I(T)P Thomas Nelson is an International Thomson Publishing Company.

I(T)P is used under licence.

ISBN 0-17-431465-5
NPN 9 8 7 6 5 4 3 2

Printed in China

Contents

NUMBER

ALGEBRA

SHAPE, SPACE AND MEASURES

HANDLING DATA

Number

1 MULTIPLYING AND DIVIDING BY POWERS OF 10

Exercise 1A

1 760	**2** 21 700	**3** 5
4 2	**5** 9500	**6** 27
7 40	**8** 8100	**9** 2
10 57	**11** 24 000	**12** 35
13 89 000	**14** 2190	**15** 420
16 42	**17** 2700	**18** 43
19 91 000	**20** 980	**21** 25 000
22 920	**23** 88	**24** 18 700
25 700	**26** 33 000	**27** 1080
28 40	**29** 650	**30** 350

Exercise 1B

1 7	**2** 56 000	**3** 210
4 24	**5** 42	**6** 330
7 180	**8** 73	**9** 87 000
10 8910	**11** 50	**12** 94
13 91 800	**14** 320	**15** 13 000
16 1050	**17** 8900	**18** 1700
19 34	**20** 21 300	**21** 62
22 1070	**23** 4400	**24** 500
25 91 200	**26** 32	**27** 50
28 5030	**29** 4	**30** 42 000

Exercise 1C

1 712	**2** 627	**3** 42
4 2.21	**5** 79	**6** 2.13
7 3120	**8** 0.029	**9** 40
10 371	**11** 0.0015	**12** 0.7
13 0.09	**14** 0.0028	**15** 310
16 127	**17** 0.079	**18** 4.17
19 2130	**20** 27.5	**21** 0.5
22 0.41	**23** 0.0008	**24** 970
25 0.003	**26** 0.000 49	**27** 0.007 1
28 30	**29** 60.5	**30** 0.0479

Exercise 1D

1 2110	**2** 12.4	**3** 41.7
4 276	**5** 0.122	**6** 12.1
7 0.0041	**8** 12.7	**9** 0.275
10 400	**11** 0.015	**12** 0.042
13 49 800	**14** 0.0009	**15** 148
16 0.0029	**17** 50	**18** 0.08
19 0.79	**20** 4210	**21** 0.028
22 0.000 71	**23** 0.7	**24** 0.0223
25 0.213	**26** 3710	**27** 0.0003
28 3100	**29** 0.004 09	**30** 0.0049

2 MULTIPLICATION BY A 2-DIGIT NUMBER WITHOUT A CALCULATOR

Exercise 2A

1 1547	**2** 5642	**3** 8208
4 4410	**5** 12 690	**6** 3234
7 5040	**8** 26 296	**9** 3010
10 7095	**11** 20 748	**12** 4284
13 56 615	**14** 70 626	**15** 3749
16 18 975	**17** 7192	**18** 6020
19 60 352	**20** 10 266	**21** 14 582
22 58 167	**23** 19 425	**24** 30 409
25 9075	**26** 23 436	**27** £31 960
28 74 497	**29** 38 906 g	**30** 51 903

Exercise 2B

1 2960	**2** 1898	**3** 8967
4 9131	**5** 13 482	**6** 2608
7 27 072	**8** 2112	**9** 42 228
10 8112	**11** 9683	**12** 27 768
13 9009	**14** 8514	**15** 71 586
16 11 520	**17** 17 496	**18** 46 718
19 84 318	**20** 82 302	**21** 4888
22 37 387	**23** 20 748	**24** 46 342
25 56 192	**26** 7106 min	**27** 45 312
28 £238.14	**29** £17 763	**30** 36 666

3 DIVISION BY A 2-DIGIT NUMBER

Exercise 3A

1 34	**2** 89	**3** 112	**4** 33
5 76	**6** 89	**7** 93	**8** 87
9 67	**10** 59	**11** 63	**12** 79
13 55	**14** 63	**15** 98	**16** 224
17 470	**18** 472	**19** 712	**20** 324
21 210	**22** 497	**23** 243	**24** 376
25 213	**26** 647	**27** 346	**28** 843
29 468	**30** £493		

Exercise 3B

1	17	**2**	21	**3**	32	**4**	39
5	53	**6**	48	**7**	76	**8**	85
9	76	**10**	93	**11**	23	**12**	87
13	32	**14**	45	**15**	61	**16**	89
17	443	**18**	232	**19**	370	**20**	343
21	354	**22**	214	**23**	470	**24**	578
25	397	**26**	621	**27**	763	**28**	845
29	£532	**30**	849				

4 ORDERING POSITIVE AND NEGATIVE NUMBERS

Exercise 4A

1 −9, −6, −4, 0, 5, 7, 9
2 −8, −7, −4, 1, 5, 8, 10
3 7, 4, 3, −1, −5, −7, −8
4 4, 3, 0, −1, −6, −7, −8
5 −9, −4, −2, 0, 6, 9, 10
6 8, 7, 3, 1, −2, −4, −8
7 −9, −4, −1, 5, 6, 8, 9
8 10, 4, 1, −2, −4, −8, −9
9 6, 5, 2, 0, −6, −7, −9
10 −9, −5, −3, 2, 4, 7, 10
11 −7, −4, −3, 0, 6, 7, 9
12 9, 4, 3, −1, −3, −5, −6
13 7, 6, 2, 1, −4, −6, −9
14 −10, −4, −1, 0, 5, 8, 10
15 −8, −6, −4, −1, 2, 5, 6
16 4, 2, 1, 0, −5, −6, −9
17 −9, −4, −3, 0, 3, 4, 7
18 −8, −5, −2, −1, 2, 3, 7
19 6, 4, 3, −1, −4, −5, −8
20 0, −2, −3, −6, −8, −9
21 10, 4, 1, −3, −7, −8, −9
22 −6, −4, −2, 0, 5, 7, 8
23 25, 18, 4, −9, −13, −21, −29
24 −40, −27, −10, 19, 25, 33, 39
25 −53, −50, −42, −32, −21, 4, 14, 29
26 30, 22, 9, −1, −9, −18, −24
27 54, 49, 37, 19, −4, −16, −23
28 −28, −14, 3, 17, 24, 31
29 49, 32, 28, 18, −18, −31, −40
30 −33, −27, −21, −7, 9, 22, 30

Exercise 4B

1 9, 6, 5, 1, −2, −3, −8
2 −8, −5, −3, 0, 5, 6, 8
3 −9, −4, −3, −1, 0, 3
4 −7, −5, −1, 0, 1, 3, 5
5 9, 6, 4, 2, −3, −5

6 8, 5, 4, −1, −3, −7, −9
7 −10, −5, −4, 1, 3, 5, 6
8 9, 7, 6, 3, 0, −3, −4
9 −9, −4, −2, −1, 0, 1, 2
10 −8, −5, −4, 1, 2, 5, 7
11 6, 4, 3, 0, −1, −5, −6
12 −10, −5, −1, 0, 7, 8, 9
13 −9, −8, −5, −1, 4, 8
14 9, 4, 1, 0, −1, −5, −7
15 8, 5, −1, −4, −6, −7, −10
16 −6, −2, −1, 0, 1, 5, 7
17 −7, −4, −3, −1, 0, 3, 4
18 6, 3, 2, 1, −3, −5, −6
19 9, 4, 3, 0, −3, −5, −7
20 4, 2, 1, −3, −6, −8, −9
21 5, 4, 1, −2, −3, −9
22 1, 0, −3, −6, −7, −9, −10
23 8, 7, 5, 3, −3, −4, −9
24 −24, −21, −18, −9, 0, 10, 16
25 −31, −28, −22, 0, 4, 16, 20
26 −14, −9, 0, 5, 13, 18, 21
27 34, 29, 25, −4, −14, −15, −21
28 43, 32, 21, −3, −15, −19, −21
29 −27, −23, −14, 2, 19, 27, 33
30 32, 28, 15, −10, −23, −30, −38

5 NEGATIVE NUMBERS IN CONTEXT

Exercise 5A

1	7	**2**	9 BCE	**3**	£25
4	5°C	**5**	£75	**6**	104 years
7	8 floors	**8**	9	**9**	£21
10	17 m	**11**	799 years	**12**	85 CE
13	£326	**14**	32 min	**15**	44 years
16	14°	**17**	2091 years		
18	Three minutes past two				
19	0.7 kg	**20**	8°		

Exercise 5B

1	9°C	**2**	£12 500	**3**	3°C
4	10 floors	**5**	671 years	**6**	7 CE
7	27 m	**8**	£9	**9**	58 years
10	4°C	**11**	20 min		
12	5 minutes to 3				
13	19 feet	**14**	49 BCE	**15**	1470 years
16	12.19 p.m.	**17**	£55	**18**	−6.5°C
19	45 years	**20**	£305		

6 NUMBER LINES

Exercise 6A

1 A: –6, B: 4, C: –9, D: 1, E: 7, F: –2
2 G: –1, H: 5, I: –8, J: –4, K: 2, L: 8
3 M: –11, N: –2, O: 5, P: 10, Q: 3, R: –5
4 S: –10, T: 6, U: –5, V: 11, W: 1, X: 4
5 (a) 4   (b) 13   (c) 10   (d) 6
   (e) 12   (f) 7   (g) 5   (h) 6
   (i) 15   (j) 11   (k) 14   (l) 16

Exercise 6B

1 A: –9, B: –2, C: 4, D: 7, E: –6, F: 0
2 G: 6, H: –4, I: –7, J: 1; K: 9; L: –1
3 M: 3, N: 10, O: –6, P: –12, Q: 7, R: –1
4 S: 11; T: 5, U: –2, V: –8, W: 2, X: –10
5 (a) 6   (b) 6   (c) 16   (d) 10
   (e) 8   (f) 13   (g) 15   (h) 11
   (i) 13   (j) 7   (k) 13   (l) 21

7 NEGATIVE NUMBERS: ADDITION AND SUBTRACTION

Exercise 7A

1 +4	2 0	3 0	4 +5
5 –1	6 +2	7 –2	8 +3
9 –7	10 +2	11 +2	12 +4
13 +3	14 –12	15 –9	16 –9
17 +1	18 –2	19 +1	20 +15
21 –4	22 +1	23 –35	24 –7
25 –42	26 +21	27 –3	28 –34
29 +5	30 –15		

Exercise 7B

1 +3	2 –2	3 0	4 0
5 –5	6 –3	7 –2	8 –5
9 –3	10 +7	11 +2	12 +7
13 +3	14 +5	15 –3	16 +5
17 +9	18 +5	19 –1	20 +14
21 +5	22 +3	23 –29	24 –8
25 0	26 +9	27 –8	28 0
29 –42	30 +41		

8 NEGATIVE NUMBERS: MULTIPLICATION AND DIVISION

Exercise 8A

1 +10	2 –24	3 –24	4 –12
5 –2	6 –5	7 –2	8 –3
9 –5	10 +5	11 –24	12 –2
13 +56	14 –5	15 +27	16 –27
17 –4	18 –16	19 –4	20 +28
21 +10	22 +9	23 –8	24 –56
25 +3	26 –6	27 –154	28 +3
29 –4	30 +108		

Exercise 8B

1 +14	2 –12	3 –7	4 +5
5 –48	6 –6	7 –2	8 +36
9 –77	10 +4	11 +42	12 +2
13 –3	14 +24	15 +36	16 –5
17 –3	18 –7	19 +2	20 +32
21 +5	22 –12	23 –3	24 +4
25 –24	26 –2	27 –5	28 –81
29 –4	30 –90		

9 NEGATIVE NUMBERS: MIXED EXAMPLES

Exercise 9A

1 +3	2 –2	3 +7	4 –3
5 +6	6 –1	7 –18	8 +5
9 –2	10 –2	11 +6	12 +6
13 +1	14 –3	15 –3	16 +3
17 –6	18 –12	19 –8	20 –4
21 –6	22 +12	23 –35	24 –2
25 –4	26 –2	27 +4	28 –4
29 +7	30 –35		

Exercise 9B

1 –2	2 –3	3 –8	4 +24
5 +5	6 +9	7 –7	8 –9
9 +11	10 +4	11 –6	12 –9
13 –4	14 +4	15 +20	16 +6
17 –8	18 +4	19 +10	20 –1
21 –3	22 –11	23 0	24 +18
25 –7	26 –11	27 –1	28 –4
29 –16	30 +32		

10 THE VALUE OF A DIGIT WITHIN A DECIMAL NUMBER

Exercise 10A

1 (a) 0.4, 0.007   (b) $\frac{4}{10}, \frac{7}{1000}$

2 (a) 0.08, 0.0005   (b) $\frac{8}{100}, \frac{5}{10\,000}$

3 (a) 0.4, 0.006   (b) $\frac{4}{10}, \frac{6}{1000}$

4 (a) 0.09, 0.0002   (b) $\frac{9}{100}, \frac{2}{10\,000}$

5 (a) 0.007, 0.0009   (b) $\frac{7}{1000}, \frac{9}{10\,000}$

6 (a) 0.04, 0.0001   (b) $\frac{4}{100}, \frac{1}{10\,000}$

7 (a) 0.007, 0.0002   (b) $\dfrac{7}{1000}, \dfrac{2}{10\,000}$

8 (a) 0.08, 0.0001   (b) $\dfrac{8}{100}, \dfrac{1}{10\,000}$

9 (a) 0.001, 0.00002   (b) $\dfrac{1}{1000}, \dfrac{2}{100\,000}$

10 (a) 0.09, 0.004   (b) $\dfrac{9}{100}, \dfrac{4}{1000}$

11 (a) 0.1, 0.002   (b) $\dfrac{1}{10}, \dfrac{2}{1000}$

12 (a) 0.0007, 0.00006   (b) $\dfrac{7}{10\,000}, \dfrac{6}{100\,000}$

13 (a) 0.3, 0.004   (b) $\dfrac{3}{10}, \dfrac{4}{1000}$

14 (a) 0.07, 0.005   (b) $\dfrac{7}{100}, \dfrac{5}{1000}$

15 (a) 0.0001, 0.00006   (b) $\dfrac{1}{10\,000}, \dfrac{6}{100\,000}$

16 (a) 0.1, 0.003   (b) $\dfrac{1}{10}, \dfrac{3}{1000}$

17 (a) 0.03, 0.002   (b) $\dfrac{3}{100}, \dfrac{2}{1000}$

18 (a) 0.01, 0.004   (b) $\dfrac{1}{100}, \dfrac{4}{1000}$

19 (a) 0.007, 0.0009   (b) $\dfrac{7}{1000}, \dfrac{9}{10\,000}$

20 (a) 0.005, 0.00009   (b) $\dfrac{5}{1000}, \dfrac{9}{100\,000}$

21 (a) 0.006, 0.0005   (b) $\dfrac{6}{1000}, \dfrac{5}{10\,000}$

22 (a) 0.0009, 0.00003   (b) $\dfrac{9}{10\,000}, \dfrac{3}{100\,000}$

23 (a) 0.001, 0.00002   (b) $\dfrac{1}{1000}, \dfrac{2}{100\,000}$

24 (a) 0.02, 0.0009   (b) $\dfrac{2}{100}, \dfrac{9}{10\,000}$

25 (a) 0.4, 0.04   (b) $\dfrac{4}{10}, \dfrac{4}{100}$

26 (a) 0.005, 0.00004   (b) $\dfrac{5}{1000}, \dfrac{4}{100\,000}$

27 (a) 0.00001, 0.000003   (b) $\dfrac{1}{100\,000}, \dfrac{3}{1\,000\,000}$

28 (a) 0.8, 0.05   (b) $\dfrac{8}{10}, \dfrac{5}{100}$

29 (a) 0.009, 0.00007   (b) $\dfrac{9}{1000}, \dfrac{7}{100\,000}$

30 (a) 0.01, 0.0002   (b) $\dfrac{1}{100}, \dfrac{2}{10\,000}$

Exercise 10B

1 (a) 0.5, 0.007   (b) $\dfrac{5}{10}, \dfrac{7}{1000}$

2 (a) 0.003, 0.0005   (b) $\dfrac{3}{1000}, \dfrac{5}{10\,000}$

3 (a) 0.9, 0.0003   (b) $\dfrac{9}{10}, \dfrac{3}{10\,000}$

4 (a) 0.03, 0.005   (b) $\dfrac{3}{100}, \dfrac{5}{1000}$

5 (a) 0.07, 0.0003   (b) $\dfrac{7}{100}, \dfrac{3}{10\,000}$

6 (a) 0.08, 0.009   (b) $\dfrac{8}{100}, \dfrac{9}{1000}$

7 (a) 0.007, 0.0009   (b) $\dfrac{7}{1000}, \dfrac{9}{10\,000}$

8 (a) 0.07, 0.0006   (b) $\dfrac{7}{100}, \dfrac{6}{10\,000}$

9 (a) 0.002, 0.00003   (b) $\dfrac{2}{1000}, \dfrac{3}{100\,000}$

10 (a) 0.3, 0.09   (b) $\dfrac{3}{10}, \dfrac{9}{100}$

11 (a) 0.005, 0.00004   (b) $\dfrac{5}{1000}, \dfrac{4}{100\,000}$

12 (a) 0.5, 0.003   (b) $\dfrac{5}{10}, \dfrac{3}{1000}$

13 (a) 0.0007, 0.00005   (b) $\dfrac{7}{10\,000}, \dfrac{5}{100\,000}$

14 (a) 0.006, 0.0004   (b) $\dfrac{6}{1000}, \dfrac{4}{10\,000}$

15 (a) 0.009, 0.00007   (b) $\dfrac{9}{1000}, \dfrac{7}{100\,000}$

16 (a) 0.01, 0.0005   (b) $\dfrac{1}{100}, \dfrac{5}{10\,000}$

17 (a) 0.1, 0.009   (b) $\dfrac{1}{10}, \dfrac{9}{1000}$

18 (a) 0.02, 0.0004   (b) $\dfrac{2}{100}, \dfrac{4}{10\,000}$

19 (a) 0.0009, 0.00005   (b) $\dfrac{9}{10\,000}, \dfrac{5}{100\,000}$

20 (a) 0.04, 0.0003   (b) $\dfrac{4}{100}, \dfrac{3}{10\,000}$

21 (a) 0.0004, 0.00005   (b) $\dfrac{4}{10\,000}, \dfrac{5}{100\,000}$

22 (a) 0.5, 0.006   (b) $\dfrac{5}{10}, \dfrac{6}{1000}$

23 (a) 0.006, 0.00004   (b) $\dfrac{6}{1000}, \dfrac{4}{100\,000}$

24 (a) 0.06, 0.0005   (b) $\dfrac{6}{100}, \dfrac{5}{10\,000}$

25 (a) 0.008, 0.00007   (b) $\dfrac{8}{1000}, \dfrac{7}{100\,000}$

26 (a) 0.009, 0.0005   (b) $\dfrac{9}{1000}, \dfrac{5}{10\,000}$

27 (a) 0.04, 0.002   (b) $\dfrac{4}{100}, \dfrac{2}{1000}$

28 (a) 0.01, 0.0006   (b) $\dfrac{1}{100}, \dfrac{6}{10\,000}$

29 (a) 0.02, 0.0003   (b) $\dfrac{2}{100}, \dfrac{3}{10\,000}$

30 (a) 0.003, 0.0007   (b) $\dfrac{3}{1000}, \dfrac{7}{10\,000}$

11 ROUNDING TO DECIMAL PLACES

Exercise 11A

#	(a)	(b)	(c)
1	4.3	4.31	4.313
2	2.4	2.36	2.362
3	2.3	2.32	2.316
4	6.4	6.41	6.408
5	8.7	8.71	8.715
6	8.1	8.07	8.072
7	4.2	4.17	4.173
8	4.2	4.19	4.193
9	8.4	8.39	8.389
10	4.5	4.52	4.516
11	9.5	9.54	9.536
12	6.9	6.90	6.902
13	10.9	10.86	10.862
14	4.0	3.96	3.960
15	13.6	13.58	13.580
16	30.0	29.96	29.956
17	7.2	7.24	7.244
18	6.2	6.20	6.205
19	10.8	10.78	10.776
20	4.5	4.51	4.513
21	3.2	3.22	3.218
22	3.8	3.84	3.844
23	28.9	28.92	28.923

24	(a) 7.9	(b) 7.88	(c) 7.878
25	(a) 10.9	(b) 10.87	(c) 10.872
26	(a) 8.1	(b) 8.12	(c) 8.121
27	(a) 5.4	(b) 5.39	(c) 5.389
28	(a) 2.4	(b) 2.39	(c) 2.387
29	(a) 3.3	(b) 3.33	(c) 3.335
30	(a) 5.9	(b) 5.92	(c) 5.917

Exercise 11B

1	(a) 54.0	(b) 53.99	(c) 53.987
2	(a) 4.7	(b) 4.73	(c) 4.729
3	(a) 7.2	(b) 7.15	(c) 7.152
4	(a) 6.3	(b) 6.28	(c) 6.279
5	(a) 10.2	(b) 10.22	(c) 10.216
6	(a) 32.3	(b) 32.26	(c) 32.256
7	(a) 90.9	(b) 90.89	(c) 90.888
8	(a) 17.5	(b) 17.45	(c) 17.452
9	(a) 25.3	(b) 25.31	(c) 25.313
10	(a) 3.2	(b) 3.23	(c) 3.225
11	(a) 3.2	(b) 3.16	(c) 3.155
12	(a) 13.3	(b) 13.28	(c) 13.279
13	(a) 7.4	(b) 7.36	(c) 7.357
14	(a) 28.4	(b) 28.44	(c) 28.441
15	(a) 36.2	(b) 36.16	(c) 36.160
16	(a) 2.4	(b) 2.36	(c) 2.365
17	(a) 4.1	(b) 4.08	(c) 4.084
18	(a) 3.0	(b) 3.02	(c) 3.018
19	(a) 2.3	(b) 2.30	(c) 2.302
20	(a) 75.2	(b) 75.18	(c) 75.180
21	(a) 12.8	(b) 12.76	(c) 12.762
22	(a) 3.4	(b) 3.36	(c) 3.361
23	(a) 2.3	(b) 2.31	(c) 2.310
24	(a) 1.2	(b) 1.18	(c) 1.182
25	(a) 2.5	(b) 2.50	(c) 2.502
26	(a) 8.4	(b) 8.41	(c) 8.414
27	(a) 1.0	(b) 1.00	(c) 1.004
28	(a) 5.0	(b) 5.03	(c) 5.030
29	(a) 7.3	(b) 7.30	(c) 7.300
30	(a) 5.7	(b) 5.69	(c) 5.689

12 ORDERING DECIMAL NUMBERS

Exercise 12A

1 0.41, 0.42, 0.49
2 0.18, 0.32, 0.91
3 0.222, 0.432, 0.794, 0.914
4 0.1042, 0.2143, 0.8132, 0.9141
5 0.012, 0.022, 0.039
6 0.2, 0.3, 0.8, 0.9
7 0.012, 0.132, 0.232
8 0.001, 0.01, 0.1
9 0.2, 0.4, 0.6
10 0.011, 0.041, 0.101
11 5.009, 5.039, 5.109
12 0.009, 0.0999, 0.9
13 13.123, 13.321, 13.331
14 4.011, 4.101, 4.111
15 4.0059, 4.0089, 4.009
16 0.23, 0.32, 2.3, 3.2
17 9.099, 9.909, 9.990
18 0.02, 0.2, 0.22, 2.2
19 231.39, 231.42, 232.01
20 0.009 99, 0.0109, 0.0199
21 0.214, 0.241, 0.252, 0.254
22 0.04, 0.75, 4.0, 6.7
23 0.125, 0.525, 0.55, 1.25
24 5.202, 5.204, 5.305, 5.306
25 5.08, 8.08, 8.8, 9.8
26 0.011, 0.110, 1.0, 1.01
27 5.623, 5.754, 6.554, 6.556
28 0.003, 0.03, 0.3, 3.0
29 9.804, 9.9, 9.904, 9.99
30 1.10, 1.12, 11.1, 11.3

Exercise 12B

1 0.3, 0.4, 0.7
2 0.111, 0.234, 0.849, 0.915
3 0.1, 0.4, 0.7, 0.9
4 0.2024, 0.3143, 0.7040, 0.8247
5 0.52, 0.53, 0.59
6 0.19, 0.23, 0.81
7 0.024, 0.156, 0.204
8 0.022, 0.052, 0.102
9 0.023, 0.033, 0.048
10 0.2, 0.002, 0.0222
11 0.004, 0.04, 0.4
12 23.123, 23.321, 23.331
13 2.0037, 2.0067, 2.007
14 3.007, 3.037, 3.107
15 0.006 66, 0.0206, 0.0266
16 0.07, 0.7, 0.77, 7.7
17 7.088, 7.808, 7.888
18 0.12, 0.21, 1.2, 2.1
19 3.033, 3.303, 3.330
20 1.08, 9.08, 9.8, 10.8
21 0.456, 0.465, 0.472, 0.474
22 0.008, 0.08, 0.8, 8.0
23 4.512, 4.643, 6.443, 6.448
24 0.03, 0.75, 3.0, 5.7
25 8.701, 8.8, 8.801, 8.88
26 4.32, 4.42, 5.02, 5.52
27 0.125, 0.626, 0.66, 1.25

28 8.80, 8.83, 88.1, 88.5
29 6.202, 6.204, 6.305, 6.306
30 0.022, 0.220, 2.0, 2.02

13 ROUNDING TO SIGNIFICANT FIGURES

Exercise 13A

1 (a) 3	(b) 3.1	(c) 3.11
2 (a) 0.4	(b) 0.36	(c) 0.358
3 (a) 3	(b) 2.6	(c) 2.65
4 (a) 0.8	(b) 0.75	(c) 0.754
5 (a) 3	(b) 3.3	(c) 3.35
6 (a) 0.4	(b) 0.36	(c) 0.365
7 (a) 0.03	(b) 0.025	(c) 0.0255
8 (a) 3	(b) 2.8	(c) 2.85
9 (a) 0.04	(b) 0.037	(c) 0.0369
10 (a) 2	(b) 2.2	(c) 2.17
11 (a) 10	(b) 15	(c) 14.5
12 (a) 50	(b) 50	(c) 49.6
13 (a) 50	(b) 46	(c) 46.2
14 (a) 300	(b) 250	(c) 255
15 (a) 500	(b) 480	(c) 484
16 (a) 200	(b) 150	(c) 151
17 (a) 200	(b) 200	(c) 198
18 (a) 400	(b) 370	(c) 375
19 (a) 40	(b) 42	(c) 42.2
20 (a) 0.05	(b) 0.045	(c) 0.0453
21 (a) 70	(b) 70	(c) 70.0
22 (a) 0.5	(b) 0.55	(c) 0.548
23 (a) 8	(b) 8.2	(c) 8.19
24 (a) 0.08	(b) 0.079	(c) 0.0789
25 (a) 2	(b) 1.5	(c) 1.52
26 (a) 100	(b) 130	(c) 129
27 (a) 2000	(b) 2300	(c) 2260
28 (a) 300	(b) 280	(c) 282
29 (a) 8000	(b) 8400	(c) 8360
30 (a) 3000	(b) 2700	(c) 2690

Exercise 13B

1 (a) 3	(b) 3.4	(c) 3.42
2 (a) 0.6	(b) 0.63	(c) 0.631
3 (a) 1	(b) 1.3	(c) 1.33
4 (a) 0.9	(b) 0.92	(c) 0.921
5 (a) 0.03	(b) 0.029	(c) 0.0292
6 (a) 0.4	(b) 0.36	(c) 0.363
7 (a) 0.08	(b) 0.077	(c) 0.0774
8 (a) 0.9	(b) 0.87	(c) 0.875
9 (a) 1	(b) 1.1	(c) 1.11
10 (a) 7	(b) 7.1	(c) 7.12
11 (a) 200	(b) 190	(c) 187

12 (a) 100	(b) 96	(c) 96.1
13 (a) 70	(b) 71	(c) 71.3
14 (a) 0.02	(b) 0.018	(c) 0.0176
15 (a) 1	(b) 1.0	(c) 1.02
16 (a) 30	(b) 33	(c) 32.8
17 (a) 90	(b) 91	(c) 90.7
18 (a) 400	(b) 400	(c) 397
19 (a) 1	(b) 0.96	(c) 0.964
20 (a) 0.05	(b) 0.052	(c) 0.0524
21 (a) 200	(b) 210	(c) 213
22 (a) 100	(b) 110	(c) 115
23 (a) 10	(b) 13	(c) 12.9
24 (a) 2000	(b) 2300	(c) 2300
25 (a) 1000	(b) 1500	(c) 1490
26 (a) 700	(b) 690	(c) 692
27 (a) 4000	(b) 4100	(c) 4060
28 (a) 400	(b) 410	(c) 409
29 (a) 5000	(b) 4800	(c) 4780
30 (a) 6000	(b) 6400	(c) 6420

14 EVALUATING POWERS

Exercise 14A

1 9	**2** 64	**3** 36	**4** 128
5 1024	**6** 81	**7** 49	**8** 1000
9 243	**10** 121	**11** 81	**12** 169
13 4096	**14** 3375	**15** 400	**16** 4
17 9	**18** 6	**19** 5	**20** 3
21 2	**22** 6912	**23** 4145	**24** 576
25 432	**26** 3189	**27** 131	**28** 4608
29 1552	**30** 104		

Exercise 14B

1 25	**2** 216	**3** 32	**4** 16
5 1296	**6** 100	**7** 343	**8** 64
9 729	**10** 10 000	**11** 6561	**12** 2187
13 196	**14** 2401	**15** 256	**16** 8
17 8	**18** 3	**19** 5	**20** 4
21 3	**22** 8192	**23** 634	**24** 945
25 2048	**26** 7801	**27** 272	**28** 43 904
29 262	**30** 972		

REVISION

Exercise A

1 (a) 5200	(b) 350	(c) 43 000	(d) 140
2 (a) 330	(b) 0.045	(c) 170	(d) 2.514
3 (a) 3556	(b) 2884	(c) 25 935	(d) 24 136
4 (a) 249	(b) 305	(c) 471	(d) 503

5 (a) −8, −3, 0, 1, 5, 6, 8
(b) −10, −7, −2, −1, 3, 7, 9

6 (a) 9, 6, 4, 1, −3, −5, −6
(b) 10, 5, 4, 0, −2, −6, −7, −9

7 (a) −3   (b) +9   (c) +8   (d) +6
(e) +15   (f) +2   (g) +2   (h) −9
(i) −3   (j) −12   (k) −6   (l) −4

8 (a) (i) 0.4, 0.007   (ii) $\frac{4}{10}$, $\frac{7}{1000}$

(b) (i) 0.04, 0.0002   (ii) $\frac{4}{100}$, $\frac{2}{10\,000}$

(c) (i) 0.007, 0.000 002   (ii) $\frac{7}{1000}$, $\frac{2}{1\,000\,000}$

(d) (i) 0.2, 0.0007   (ii) $\frac{2}{10}$, $\frac{7}{10\,000}$

9 (a) 0.12, 0.2, 0.22, 0.222
(b) 0.104, 0.14, 0.401, 1.104
(c) 3.030, 3.303, 3.330, 3.333
(d) 0.1568, 0.1658, 0.1685, 0.1856

10 (a) (i) 1.4   (ii) 1.35   (iii) 1.354
(b) (i) 15.1   (ii) 15.09   (iii) 15.091
(c) (i) 6.8   (ii) 6.80   (iii) 6.799

11 (a) (i) 5   (ii) 4.6   (iii) 4.58
(b) (i) 40   (ii) 37   (iii) 36.9
(c) (i) 2000   (ii) 1800   (iii) 1840

12 (a) 625   (b) 512   (c) 27   (d) 36
(e) 50 625   (f) 755   (g) 87   (h) 292

Exercise AA

1 15   **2** 4000
3 £300   **4** 12 000
5 6240   **6** 1848
7 6240   **8** 19 180
9 125   **10** 24
11 214   **12** 603
13 −4°C   **14** 210 years
15 £39   **16** 8°

15 EQUIVALENT FRACTIONS

Exercise 15A

1 $\frac{1}{2} = \frac{2}{4} = \frac{3}{6} = \frac{4}{8}$

2 $\frac{2}{5} = \frac{6}{15} = \frac{10}{25} = \frac{12}{30}$

3 $\frac{5}{6} = \frac{10}{12} = \frac{20}{24} = \frac{25}{30}$

4 $\frac{3}{4} = \frac{6}{8} = \frac{9}{12} = \frac{15}{20}$

5 $\frac{1}{5} = \frac{3}{15} = \frac{5}{25} = \frac{7}{35}$

6 $\frac{5}{9} = \frac{10}{18} = \frac{15}{27} = \frac{30}{54}$

7 $\frac{3}{8} = \frac{6}{16} = \frac{9}{24} = \frac{12}{32}$

8 $\frac{1}{7} = \frac{3}{21} = \frac{5}{35} = \frac{7}{49} = \frac{9}{63}$

9 $\frac{7}{10} = \frac{21}{30} = \frac{28}{40} = \frac{49}{70} = \frac{70}{100}$

10 $\frac{7}{8} = \frac{14}{16} = \frac{21}{24} = \frac{35}{40} = \frac{49}{56}$

11 $\frac{9}{20} = \frac{18}{40} = \frac{27}{60} = \frac{63}{140} = \frac{72}{160}$

12 $\frac{13}{24} = \frac{26}{48} = \frac{39}{72} = \frac{52}{96} = \frac{65}{120}$

Exercise 15B

1 $\frac{1}{3} = \frac{3}{9} = \frac{5}{15} = \frac{6}{18}$

2 $\frac{5}{8} = \frac{10}{16} = \frac{15}{24} = \frac{20}{32}$

3 $\frac{3}{5} = \frac{6}{10} = \frac{9}{15} = \frac{15}{25}$

4 $\frac{1}{6} = \frac{2}{12} = \frac{4}{24} = \frac{5}{30}$

5 $\frac{7}{9} = \frac{21}{27} = \frac{35}{45} = \frac{49}{63}$

6 $\frac{3}{10} = \frac{9}{30} = \frac{12}{40} = \frac{18}{60}$

7 $\frac{1}{8} = \frac{2}{16} = \frac{5}{40} = \frac{6}{48} = \frac{8}{64}$

8 $\frac{5}{12} = \frac{15}{36} = \frac{25}{60} = \frac{35}{84} = \frac{45}{108}$

9 $\frac{5}{24} = \frac{10}{48} = \frac{20}{96} = \frac{30}{144} = \frac{35}{168}$

10 $\frac{5}{32} = \frac{15}{96} = \frac{25}{160} = \frac{30}{192} = \frac{35}{224}$

11 $\frac{7}{20} = \frac{28}{80} = \frac{35}{100} = \frac{56}{160} = \frac{70}{200}$

12 $\frac{4}{15} = \frac{8}{30} = \frac{20}{75} = \frac{24}{90} = \frac{32}{120}$

16 FRACTIONS OF QUANTITIES

Exercise 16A

1 6   **2** 24   **3** 2
4 4p   **5** 5 g   **6** £1.50
7 24 km   **8** £4   **9** 2.8 kg
10 £21.30   **11** 15 m   **12** 4.96 m
13 32 g   **14** £22.38   **15** £3.44
16 £60   **17** 21 l   **18** £12.30
19 240 g   **20** £3.24   **21** 307.5 kg
22 £43.11   **23** £22.95   **24** £149.63
25 17.76 km   **26** £19.65   **27** 150 mm
28 £1.15   **29** £4.59   **30** 77 ml

Exercise 16B

1 4   **2** 12   **3** 8
4 56p   **5** £5   **6** 9 g
7 £3.50   **8** 30p   **9** £14.01
10 320 g   **11** 11.55 m   **12** 15 kg
13 £11.41   **14** $28   **15** £14.50
16 1.35 kg   **17** 86.45 l   **18** £2.90
19 £19.18   **20** 218 km   **21** 40 l
22 16.45 l   **23** £9.39   **24** £7.50
25 4.52 kg   **26** £41.16   **27** £10.26
28 £11.16   **29** 105 kg   **30** £38.50

17 CANCELLING FRACTIONS

Exercise 17A

1 $\frac{3}{4}$	**2** $\frac{4}{5}$	**3** $\frac{5}{6}$	**4** $\frac{3}{4}$	**5** $\frac{5}{6}$
6 $\frac{1}{2}$	**7** $\frac{3}{4}$	**8** $\frac{5}{7}$	**9** $\frac{8}{9}$	**10** $\frac{5}{11}$
11 $\frac{8}{11}$	**12** $\frac{3}{4}$	**13** $\frac{9}{16}$	**14** $\frac{3}{4}$	**15** $\frac{4}{7}$
16 $\frac{2}{3}$	**17** $\frac{2}{3}$	**18** $\frac{15}{16}$	**19** $\frac{1}{2}$	**20** $\frac{1}{7}$
21 $\frac{4}{5}$	**22** $\frac{4}{5}$	**23** $\frac{1}{2}$	**24** $\frac{3}{4}$	**25** $\frac{2}{5}$
26 $\frac{3}{4}$	**27** $\frac{1}{4}$	**28** $\frac{3}{40}$	**29** $\frac{2}{5}$	**30** $\frac{3}{7}$

Exercise 17B

1 $\frac{7}{9}$	**2** $\frac{1}{4}$	**3** $\frac{2}{3}$	**4** $\frac{1}{5}$	**5** $\frac{2}{3}$
6 $\frac{2}{3}$	**7** $\frac{5}{8}$	**8** $\frac{13}{17}$	**9** $\frac{3}{8}$	**10** $\frac{7}{10}$
11 $\frac{3}{5}$	**12** $\frac{7}{15}$	**13** $\frac{2}{5}$	**14** $\frac{4}{9}$	**15** $\frac{7}{20}$
16 $\frac{2}{3}$	**17** $\frac{3}{4}$	**18** $\frac{4}{5}$	**19** $\frac{1}{2}$	**20** $\frac{11}{12}$
21 $\frac{3}{8}$	**22** $\frac{2}{3}$	**23** $\frac{5}{16}$	**24** $\frac{2}{9}$	**25** $\frac{9}{13}$
26 $\frac{7}{10}$	**27** $\frac{19}{23}$	**28** $\frac{127}{154}$	**29** $\frac{2}{5}$	**30** $\frac{5}{9}$

18 CONVERSION TO AND FROM MIXED NUMBERS

Exercise 18A

1 $\frac{11}{3}$	**2** $\frac{3}{2}$	**3** $\frac{22}{5}$	**4** $\frac{17}{4}$	**5** $\frac{13}{4}$
6 $\frac{19}{2}$	**7** $\frac{89}{10}$	**8** $\frac{31}{11}$	**9** $\frac{31}{4}$	**10** $\frac{71}{6}$
11 $\frac{43}{7}$	**12** $\frac{68}{5}$	**13** $\frac{53}{10}$	**14** $\frac{94}{9}$	**15** $\frac{41}{7}$
16 $\frac{37}{7}$	**17** $\frac{51}{4}$	**18** $\frac{34}{7}$	**19** $\frac{39}{10}$	**20** $\frac{29}{5}$
21 $\frac{173}{18}$	**22** $\frac{68}{7}$	**23** $\frac{80}{9}$	**24** $\frac{107}{8}$	**25** $\frac{17}{12}$
26 $\frac{29}{5}$	**27** $\frac{91}{3}$	**28** $\frac{53}{12}$	**29** $\frac{157}{8}$	**30** $\frac{97}{10}$

Exercise 18B

1 $\frac{8}{3}$	**2** $\frac{7}{2}$	**3** $\frac{28}{5}$	**4** $\frac{15}{4}$	**5** $\frac{107}{12}$
6 $\frac{43}{6}$	**7** $\frac{11}{4}$	**8** $\frac{29}{4}$	**9** $\frac{31}{5}$	**10** $\frac{47}{5}$
11 $\frac{11}{6}$	**12** $\frac{81}{16}$	**13** $\frac{23}{3}$	**14** $\frac{35}{6}$	**15** $\frac{76}{9}$
16 $\frac{13}{7}$	**17** $\frac{13}{10}$	**18** $\frac{50}{7}$	**19** $\frac{72}{7}$	**20** $\frac{22}{5}$
21 $\frac{85}{9}$	**22** $\frac{149}{12}$	**23** $\frac{59}{6}$	**24** $\frac{71}{8}$	**25** $\frac{47}{12}$
26 $\frac{91}{8}$	**27** $\frac{130}{7}$	**28** $\frac{41}{12}$	**29** $\frac{115}{9}$	**30** $\frac{53}{5}$

Exercise 18C

1 $1\frac{1}{4}$	**2** $5\frac{2}{3}$	**3** $4\frac{3}{4}$	**4** $4\frac{1}{2}$
5 $1\frac{4}{5}$	**6** $6\frac{5}{6}$	**7** $5\frac{3}{7}$	**8** $2\frac{3}{4}$
9 $4\frac{1}{12}$	**10** $7\frac{5}{8}$	**11** $7\frac{3}{10}$	**12** $14\frac{5}{6}$
13 $6\frac{1}{8}$	**14** $9\frac{1}{9}$	**15** $33\frac{1}{3}$	**16** $9\frac{2}{9}$
17 $5\frac{5}{6}$	**18** $7\frac{3}{4}$	**19** $7\frac{2}{3}$	**20** $3\frac{4}{9}$
21 $5\frac{6}{7}$	**22** $7\frac{1}{8}$	**23** $8\frac{8}{15}$	**24** $21\frac{1}{6}$
25 $12\frac{1}{2}$	**26** $10\frac{2}{3}$	**27** $11\frac{1}{9}$	**28** $4\frac{9}{25}$
29 $4\frac{1}{24}$	**30** $6\frac{1}{16}$		

Exercise 18D

1 $1\frac{1}{2}$	**2** $2\frac{1}{2}$	**3** $2\frac{1}{4}$	**4** $1\frac{7}{12}$
5 $2\frac{1}{5}$	**6** $12\frac{1}{2}$	**7** $7\frac{7}{8}$	**8** $6\frac{3}{4}$
9 $5\frac{7}{10}$	**10** $4\frac{4}{5}$	**11** $9\frac{5}{8}$	**12** $1\frac{11}{12}$
13 $6\frac{6}{7}$	**14** $16\frac{4}{5}$	**15** $2\frac{2}{5}$	**16** $12\frac{3}{4}$
17 $15\frac{1}{2}$	**18** $4\frac{3}{4}$	**19** $1\frac{5}{9}$	**20** $8\frac{4}{9}$
21 $5\frac{3}{5}$	**22** $13\frac{2}{7}$	**23** $3\frac{11}{15}$	**24** $6\frac{5}{6}$
25 $15\frac{4}{5}$	**26** $6\frac{9}{14}$	**27** $2\frac{7}{20}$	**28** $5\frac{4}{25}$
29 $6\frac{7}{12}$	**30** $6\frac{1}{3}$		

19 ADDITION OF SIMPLE FRACTIONS

Exercise 19A

1 1	**2** $1\frac{1}{8}$	**3** 1	**4** 1
5 $\frac{5}{8}$	**6** $\frac{9}{16}$	**7** $\frac{5}{8}$	**8** $\frac{17}{32}$
9 $\frac{25}{32}$	**10** $\frac{13}{16}$	**11** $\frac{31}{32}$	**12** $1\frac{1}{8}$
13 $\frac{19}{32}$	**14** $1\frac{5}{8}$	**15** $1\frac{1}{4}$	**16** $1\frac{3}{16}$
17 $1\frac{7}{16}$	**18** $1\frac{1}{16}$	**19** $1\frac{9}{16}$	**20** $\frac{13}{16}$
21 $\frac{11}{12}$	**22** $1\frac{1}{2}$	**23** $1\frac{3}{10}$	**24** $\frac{7}{9}$
25 $1\frac{1}{4}$	**26** $1\frac{1}{6}$ kg	**27** $7\frac{3}{5}$ l	**28** $10\frac{7}{16}$ ft
29 $6\frac{3}{8}$ m	**30** $9\frac{1}{14}$ in		

Exercise 19B

1 1	**2** $1\frac{2}{7}$	**3** $1\frac{1}{7}$	**4** $1\frac{1}{3}$
5 $\frac{3}{4}$	**6** $\frac{5}{16}$	**7** $\frac{19}{32}$	**8** $\frac{5}{16}$
9 $\frac{31}{32}$	**10** $\frac{21}{32}$	**11** $\frac{5}{8}$	**12** $1\frac{3}{8}$
13 $1\frac{1}{8}$	**14** $1\frac{7}{16}$	**15** $1\frac{7}{16}$	**16** $1\frac{23}{32}$
17 $1\frac{1}{32}$	**18** $1\frac{1}{16}$	**19** $1\frac{5}{32}$	**20** $\frac{11}{16}$
21 $\frac{19}{30}$	**22** $1\frac{3}{8}$	**23** $1\frac{5}{9}$	**24** $\frac{5}{8}$
25 $\frac{7}{12}$	**26** $7\frac{5}{8}$ ft	**27** 7 kg	**28** $9\frac{4}{9}$ ft
29 $12\frac{4}{15}$ cm	**30** $10\frac{1}{3}$ hectares		

20 SUBTRACTION OF SIMPLE FRACTIONS

Exercise 20A

1 $\frac{1}{4}$	2 $\frac{15}{16}$	3 $2\frac{3}{8}$	4 $1\frac{1}{4}$
5 $\frac{3}{8}$	6 $1\frac{15}{32}$	7 $2\frac{1}{3}$	8 $6\frac{2}{9}$
9 $\frac{1}{4}$	10 $\frac{3}{8}$	11 $\frac{1}{2}$	12 $\frac{1}{8}$
13 $\frac{3}{8}$	14 $\frac{1}{16}$	15 $\frac{5}{8}$	16 $\frac{9}{20}$
17 $\frac{1}{16}$	18 $\frac{9}{16}$	19 $\frac{7}{16}$	20 $\frac{7}{32}$
21 $\frac{1}{4}$	22 $2\frac{3}{8}$	23 $\frac{1}{4}$	24 $\frac{4}{7}$
25 $2\frac{9}{20}$	26 $5\frac{1}{6}$ ft	27 $2\frac{1}{4}$ cm	28 $1\frac{1}{32}$ cm
29 $2\frac{1}{16}$ ft	30 $1\frac{3}{16}$ kg		

Exercise 20B

1 $\frac{5}{8}$	2 $1\frac{7}{8}$	3 $5\frac{1}{16}$	4 $\frac{1}{32}$
5 $2\frac{15}{32}$	6 $5\frac{5}{16}$	7 $1\frac{1}{5}$	8 $4\frac{2}{5}$
9 $\frac{5}{12}$	10 $\frac{1}{4}$	11 $\frac{1}{9}$	12 $\frac{1}{4}$
13 $\frac{3}{8}$	14 $\frac{5}{8}$	15 $\frac{5}{16}$	16 $\frac{1}{8}$
17 $\frac{17}{32}$	18 $\frac{1}{8}$	19 $\frac{1}{32}$	20 $\frac{3}{16}$
21 $2\frac{3}{8}$	22 $\frac{3}{32}$	23 $\frac{1}{5}$	24 $\frac{2}{3}$
25 $1\frac{1}{8}$	26 $6\frac{3}{8}$ l	27 $3\frac{3}{8}$ kg	28 $1\frac{1}{16}$ kg
29 $1\frac{1}{32}$ ft	30 $1\frac{3}{16}$ cm		

21 SIMPLE MULTIPLICATION OF FRACTIONS

Exercise 21A

1 $\frac{8}{15}$	2 $\frac{2}{5}$	3 $\frac{3}{20}$	4 $\frac{1}{6}$	5 $\frac{3}{4}$
6 $\frac{10}{21}$	7 $\frac{2}{9}$	8 $\frac{1}{3}$	9 $\frac{1}{4}$	10 $\frac{9}{10}$
11 $\frac{1}{2}$	12 $\frac{2}{3}$	13 $\frac{2}{3}$	14 $5\frac{1}{3}$	15 $\frac{3}{4}$
16 $\frac{7}{20}$	17 $\frac{1}{2}$	18 $1\frac{1}{2}$	19 $\frac{2}{3}$	20 $\frac{2}{3}$
21 8	22 $\frac{3}{32}$	23 $\frac{8}{9}$	24 $\frac{4}{35}$	25 $\frac{7}{16}$
26 10	27 8	28 $\frac{9}{64}$	29 $6\frac{2}{3}$	30 $\frac{5}{12}$

Exercise 21B

1 $\frac{4}{21}$	2 $\frac{2}{5}$	3 $\frac{1}{7}$	4 $\frac{5}{18}$	5 $\frac{8}{21}$
6 $\frac{7}{16}$	7 $\frac{1}{2}$	8 $\frac{15}{28}$	9 $\frac{1}{12}$	10 $\frac{1}{3}$
11 $\frac{5}{14}$	12 $\frac{4}{7}$	13 $\frac{2}{3}$	14 $\frac{1}{2}$	15 $\frac{1}{12}$
16 $\frac{7}{18}$	17 $\frac{1}{9}$	18 $4\frac{4}{7}$	19 $\frac{3}{7}$	20 4
21 $\frac{8}{15}$	22 6	23 $1\frac{7}{8}$	24 $\frac{3}{70}$	25 $\frac{5}{32}$
26 $12\frac{1}{2}$	27 $\frac{11}{128}$	28 $\frac{3}{32}$	29 $5\frac{5}{8}$	30 $2\frac{1}{4}$

22 SIMPLE DIVISION OF FRACTIONS

Exercise 22A

1 $\frac{20}{27}$	2 $\frac{1}{8}$	3 $\frac{8}{15}$	4 $\frac{1}{12}$	5 $\frac{4}{45}$
6 $\frac{15}{28}$	7 $\frac{6}{7}$	8 $\frac{7}{8}$	9 $\frac{9}{11}$	10 $\frac{2}{3}$
11 $1\frac{3}{4}$	12 $\frac{2}{5}$	13 $\frac{3}{5}$	14 $\frac{2}{3}$	15 $\frac{9}{10}$
16 $\frac{1}{9}$	17 6	18 $1\frac{1}{2}$	19 $1\frac{1}{5}$	20 $2\frac{6}{7}$

Exercise 22B

1 $\frac{1}{6}$	2 $1\frac{1}{5}$	3 $\frac{1}{10}$	4 $\frac{4}{5}$	5 $\frac{16}{21}$
6 $\frac{7}{24}$	7 $\frac{3}{4}$	8 $\frac{4}{9}$	9 $\frac{3}{4}$	10 $\frac{1}{4}$
11 $1\frac{2}{5}$	12 $\frac{3}{5}$	13 $\frac{2}{3}$	14 $\frac{3}{5}$	15 $\frac{1}{18}$
16 $\frac{2}{3}$	17 $\frac{1}{8}$	18 $1\frac{1}{14}$	19 $1\frac{1}{5}$	20 $4\frac{1}{5}$

23 CONVERSION BETWEEN FRACTIONS AND DECIMALS

Exercise 23A

1 0.25	2 0.375	3 0.2
4 0.0625	5 0.5625	6 0.7
7 2.12	8 0.15	9 10.4
10 4.4	11 3.3	12 6.04
13 0.65	14 4.175	15 0.9375
16 2.35	17 0.093 75	18 4.45
19 5.95	20 2.44	21 0.3333
22 0.4545	23 0.5833	24 0.1111
25 0.6333	26 0.8333	27 0.1429
28 0.7778	29 0.0833	30 0.8182

Exercise 23B

1 0.5	2 0.125	3 0.8
4 0.05	5 0.3125	6 0.3
7 3.17	8 4.9	9 0.45
10 1.875	11 2.36	12 0.8125
13 5.4	14 0.95	15 4.525
16 4.28	17 1.52	18 0.156 25
19 5.84	20 7.325	21 0.6667
22 0.2727	23 0.4167	24 0.4444
25 0.5454	26 0.4333	27 0.5556
28 0.2857	29 0.9091	30 0.0909

Exercise 23C

1 $\frac{7}{10}$	2 $\frac{3}{100}$	3 $\frac{13}{20}$	4 $\frac{17}{20}$
5 $\frac{9}{10}$	6 $\frac{1}{25}$	7 $\frac{2}{5}$	8 $\frac{19}{20}$
9 $\frac{1}{10}$	10 $\frac{1}{8}$	11 $\frac{37}{100}$	12 $\frac{1}{500}$
13 $\frac{447}{1000}$	14 $\frac{27}{100}$	15 $\frac{7}{20}$	16 $\frac{23}{40}$

17 $\frac{51}{400}$ **18** $\frac{421}{500}$ **19** $\frac{6}{25}$ **20** $\frac{24}{25}$

21 $3\frac{9}{40}$ **22** $\frac{147}{200}$ **23** $\frac{191}{200}$ **24** $1\frac{13}{25}$

25 $\frac{1}{4}$ **26** $6\frac{17}{20}$ **27** $\frac{14}{25}$ **28** $\frac{187}{200}$

29 $2\frac{17}{80}$ **30** $5\frac{4}{5}$

Exercise 23D

1 $\frac{47}{100}$ **2** $\frac{3}{5}$ **3** $\frac{1}{5}$ **4** $\frac{1}{50}$

5 $\frac{19}{100}$ **6** $\frac{3}{8}$ **7** $\frac{99}{100}$ **8** $\frac{9}{25}$

9 $\frac{9}{50}$ **10** $\frac{7}{100}$ **11** $\frac{16}{25}$ **12** $\frac{29}{40}$

13 $\frac{11}{20}$ **14** $\frac{37}{40}$ **15** $\frac{119}{200}$ **16** $\frac{181}{200}$

17 $\frac{18}{125}$ **18** $\frac{17}{25}$ **19** $5\frac{81}{100}$ **20** $3\frac{11}{16}$

21 $\frac{167}{200}$ **22** $2\frac{11}{25}$ **23** $\frac{4}{25}$ **24** $3\frac{11}{20}$

25 $4\frac{49}{50}$ **26** $\frac{147}{200}$ **27** $2\frac{33}{80}$ **28** $1\frac{5}{16}$

29 $\frac{3}{25}$ **30** $2\frac{1}{20}$

24 CONVERSION BETWEEN DECIMALS AND PERCENTAGES

Exercise 24A

1 5%   **2** 3%   **3** $13\frac{1}{2}$%   **4** 20%

5 $1\frac{1}{4}$%   **6** 7%   **7** $23\frac{1}{2}$%   **8** 39%

9 $7\frac{1}{2}$%   **10** 9%   **11** $73\frac{1}{2}$%   **12** 40%

13 $11\frac{1}{4}$%   **14** 91%   **15** 7%   **16** $37\frac{1}{2}$%

17 $11\frac{1}{2}$%   **18** 57%   **19** 81%   **20** $20\frac{1}{2}$%

Exercise 24B

1 10%   **2** 9%   **3** $98\frac{1}{2}$%   **4** 70%

5 43%   **6** 99%   **7** 30%   **8** $21\frac{1}{2}$%

9 $32\frac{1}{2}$%   **10** 12%   **11** 89%   **12** 37%

13 73%   **14** $23\frac{1}{2}$%   **15** 71%   **16** $1\frac{1}{4}$%

17 59%   **18** $31\frac{3}{4}$%   **19** 97%   **20** $81\frac{1}{2}$%

Exercise 24C

1 0.31   **2** 0.85   **3** 0.1   **4** 0.42

5 0.16   **6** 0.5   **7** 0.57   **8** 0.02

9 0.96   **10** 0.41   **11** 0.1833   **12** 0.2175

13 0.865   **14** 0.44   **15** 0.1525   **16** 0.62

17 0.3225   **18** 0.7967   **19** 0.3175   **20** 0.495

Exercise 24D

1 0.86   **2** 0.6   **3** 0.31   **4** 0.03

5 0.53   **6** 0.3   **7** 0.82   **8** 0.42

9 0.08   **10** 0.9   **11** 0.5425   **12** 0.0467

13 0.175   **14** 0.2975   **15** 0.69   **16** 0.5933

17 0.5175   **18** 0.72   **19** 0.8025   **20** 0.595

25 CONVERSION BETWEEN FRACTIONS AND PERCENTAGES

Exercise 25A

1 60%   **2** 25%   **3** 50%   **4** 22%

5 5%   **6** 3%   **7** 42%   **8** 34%

9 15%   **10** 10%   **11** $37\frac{1}{2}$%   **12** 24%

13 62%   **14** $62\frac{1}{2}$%   **15** $1\frac{1}{4}$%   **16** 48%

17 52%   **18** $77\frac{7}{9}$%   **19** $85\frac{5}{7}$%   **20** $11\frac{1}{4}$%

Exercise 25B

1 30%   **2** 75%   **3** 18%   **4** 1%

5 $7\frac{1}{2}$%   **6** 7%   **7** 70%   **8** $47\frac{1}{2}$%

9 55%   **10** $87\frac{1}{2}$%   **11** 68%   **12** 90%

13 19%   **14** $12\frac{1}{2}$%   **15** $32\frac{1}{2}$%   **16** $18\frac{2}{11}$%

17 31%   **18** $41\frac{2}{3}$%   **19** $56\frac{1}{4}$%   **20** $23\frac{17}{21}$%

Exercise 25C

1 $\frac{3}{10}$ **2** $\frac{1}{100}$ **3** $\frac{1}{20}$ **4** $\frac{21}{50}$ **5** $\frac{3}{20}$

6 $\frac{3}{100}$ **7** $\frac{3}{4}$ **8** $\frac{99}{100}$ **9** $\frac{16}{25}$ **10** $\frac{49}{100}$

11 $\frac{14}{25}$ **12** $\frac{12}{25}$ **13** $\frac{4}{25}$ **14** $\frac{19}{20}$ **15** $\frac{17}{25}$

16 $\frac{5}{8}$ **17** $\frac{1}{8}$ **18** $\frac{1}{6}$ **19** $\frac{3}{40}$ **20** $\frac{1}{12}$

Exercise 25D

1 $\frac{1}{10}$ **2** $\frac{3}{100}$ **3** $\frac{11}{20}$ **4** $\frac{3}{5}$ **5** $\frac{7}{100}$

6 $\frac{1}{4}$ **7** $\frac{41}{100}$ **8** $\frac{4}{5}$ **9** $\frac{77}{100}$ **10** $\frac{7}{20}$

11 $\frac{6}{25}$ **12** $\frac{17}{100}$ **13** $\frac{9}{20}$ **14** $\frac{3}{25}$ **15** $\frac{31}{100}$

16 $\frac{1}{40}$ **17** $\frac{7}{8}$ **18** $\frac{3}{8}$ **19** $\frac{17}{200}$ **20** $\frac{29}{300}$

26 CALCULATING PERCENTAGES OF QUANTITIES

Exercise 26A

1 £18   **2** £22   **3** 45 m   **4** £57

5 $7\frac{1}{2}$ kg   **6** £84   **7** 300 kg   **8** 54 t

9 5p   **10** 25   **11** 40.5 m   **12** 204

13 £1.70   **14** £3   **15** 35p   **16** 40

17 £120   **18** £1.50   **19** 12.8 kg   **20** £17.25

21 34p   **22** 17.6 m   **23** 30   **24** 3.6 m

25 12 g   **26** £2.22   **27** 15 km   **28** £6.72

29 34p   **30** 30p

Exercise 26B

1 10.2 t   **2** £49   **3** £40   **4** 21 m

5 37.5 g   **6** 48 kg   **7** £99   **8** 3.75 m

9 11.9 m   **10** 50   **11** £1.17   **12** £120

13 49   **14** £3.25   **15** £6   **16** £42

17 10.8 kg   **18** £14.70   **19** 2 kg   **20** 10.8 kg

21 192   22 40   23 1.5 g   24 £120
25 £1.30   26 30   27 4   28 10 g
29 44p   30 £22

27 FRACTIONAL CHANGES

Exercise 27A

1 24	**2** 28	**3** 25	**4** 24
5 42	**6** 40	**7** 30	**8** 12
9 21	**10** 6	**11** 150	**12** 4
13 45	**14** 72	**15** 8	**16** 95
17 $40	**18** 27	**19** 10	**20** 121
21 91	**22** 20	**23** $6	**24** 66
25 80	**26** £1.90	**27** 76	**28** 5p
29 £7.65	**30** £35.31		

Exercise 27B

1 12	**2** 24	**3** 66	**4** 15
5 16	**6** 18	**7** 25	**8** 8
9 6	**10** 42	**11** 104	**12** 9
13 14	**14** 55	**15** 75	**16** 20
17 25	**18** 20	**19** 130	**20** 15
21 22	**22** 55	**23** £1.30	**24** £36
25 105	**26** 77	**27** £119	**28** 28
29 £9.17	**30** £11.13		

28 ONE NUMBER AS A FRACTION OF ANOTHER

Exercise 28A

1 $\frac{1}{8}$	**2** $\frac{1}{2}$	**3** $\frac{3}{13}$	**4** $\frac{2}{17}$	**5** $\frac{1}{12}$
6 $\frac{3}{7}$	**7** $\frac{1}{17}$	**8** $\frac{1}{3}$	**9** $\frac{6}{7}$	**10** $\frac{7}{13}$
11 $\frac{3}{8}$	**12** $\frac{1}{27}$	**13** $\frac{4}{7}$	**14** $\frac{1}{5}$	**15** $\frac{2}{17}$
16 $\frac{3}{8}$	**17** $\frac{1}{6}$	**18** $\frac{3}{23}$	**19** $\frac{8}{125}$	**20** $\frac{1}{50}$

Exercise 28B

1 $\frac{3}{7}$	**2** $\frac{2}{3}$	**3** $\frac{2}{7}$	**4** $\frac{1}{3}$	**5** $\frac{1}{9}$
6 $\frac{5}{14}$	**7** $\frac{1}{2}$	**8** $\frac{5}{13}$	**9** $\frac{4}{7}$	**10** $\frac{5}{17}$
11 $\frac{1}{15}$	**12** $\frac{1}{4}$	**13** $\frac{4}{5}$	**14** $\frac{1}{4}$	**15** $\frac{1}{10}$
16 $\frac{7}{33}$	**17** $\frac{4}{25}$	**18** $\frac{5}{12}$	**19** $\frac{8}{45}$	**20** $\frac{1}{75}$

29 PERCENTAGE CHANGE

Exercise 29A

1 315	**2** 480	**3** £230.40
4 £1.20	**5** 624	**6** £44.08
7 £60.30	**8** 72 km	**9** 231 ml
10 £777	**11** 112.8 m	**12** £325
13 36 km	**4** £1.58	**15** 2.5 g
16 1120 kg	**17** 51 g	**18** £2.85
19 1584 mm	**20** £4.80	**21** 42p
22 £44.08	**23** 1312 m	**24** £7.22
25 £8.19	**26** £13 504	**27** £89.07
28 £33.60	**29** 63 600	**30** £2625

Exercise 29B

1 420	**2** £9.50	**3** £46
4 420	**5** £252	**6** £523.20
7 £40.05	**8** 40p	**9** 438 cm
10 2312.5 g	**11** 420 ml	**12** £8.88
13 £39.84	**14** 4.95 km	**15** £2.08
16 £1.73	**17** 1040 g	**18** 1179 km
19 £2.62	**20** 114 ml	**21** £2.10
22 £1.54	**23** £13.13	**24** £20.93
25 £41.13	**26** £531.25	**27** £144
28 £103.40	**29** £8118.13	**30** £240.35

30 ONE NUMBER AS A PERCENTAGE OF ANOTHER

Exercise 30A

1 30%	**2** $12\frac{1}{2}$%	**3** 8%	**4** 5%
5 30%	**6** $37\frac{1}{2}$%	**7** 16%	**8** 74%
9 $7\frac{1}{2}$%	**10** $33\frac{3}{4}$%	**11** 30%	**12** 2%
13 $3\frac{1}{3}$%	**14** 15%	**15** 40%	**16** 70%
17 $62\frac{1}{2}$%	**18** $37\frac{1}{2}$%	**19** $53\frac{1}{3}$%	**20** 30%
21 $43\frac{1}{3}$%	**22** 13.6%	**23** $3\frac{1}{3}$%	**24** $17\frac{1}{2}$%
25 $68\frac{3}{4}$%	**26** 10%	**27** 78%	**28** 96.8%
29 $1\frac{2}{3}$%	**30** $63\frac{1}{3}$%		

Exercise 30B

1 50%	**2** 5%	**3** 85%	**4** 33.6%
5 8%	**6** 15%	**7** 24%	**8** 8%
9 20%	**10** 28%	**11** 35%	**12** 56%
13 $7\frac{1}{2}$%	**14** $18\frac{1}{2}$%	**15** 30%	**16** $16\frac{2}{3}$%
17 $12\frac{1}{2}$%	**18** $6\frac{1}{4}$%	**19** $8\frac{1}{3}$%	**20** 20%
21 $6\frac{2}{3}$%	**22** $31\frac{1}{4}$%	**23** $66\frac{2}{3}$%	**24** 15%
25 $62\frac{1}{2}$%	**26** 95%	**27** $93\frac{3}{4}$%	**28** 38%
29 5%	**30** 40%		

31 RATIO

Exercise 31A

1 3:4	**2** 1:5	**3** 2:3	**4** 7:30
5 7:2	**6** 2:1	**7** 2:7	**8** 3:5

9 1:6	**10** 1:4	**11** 15:2	**12** 8:15
13 3:10	**14** 4:5	**15** 33:100	**16** 2:3
17 10:3	**18** 7:6	**19** 2:3	**20** 9:11
21 500:1	**22** 7:10	**23** 1:1.25	**24** 1:5
25 1:1.2	**26** 1:4	**27** 1:0.75	**28** 1:1.5
29 $1:3\frac{1}{3}$	**30** 1:1.6		

Exercise 31B

1 1:3	**2** 1:3	**3** 1:2	**4** 2:3
5 2:5	**6** 3:1	**7** 4:7	**8** 1:16
9 2:1	**10** 3:8	**11** 3:10	**12** 2:3
13 7:6	**14** 29:40	**15** 5:9	**16** 17:20
17 2:3	**18** 1:2	**19** 8:3	**20** 5:1
21 1:2	**22** 20:1	**23** 1:0.75	**24** 1:0.5
25 1:7.5	**26** 1:0.2	**27** 1:7.75	**28** 1:0.6
29 $1:1\frac{1}{9}$	**30** $1:\frac{2}{3}$		

32 USING RATIOS

Exercise 32A

1 12	**2** 3	**3** 30	**4** 4
5 4	**6** 30	**7** 12	**8** 7
9 12	**10** 15	**11** 7	**12** 6
13 1	**14** 24	**15** 5	**16** 9
17 4	**18** 40	**19** 42	**20** 9
21 18 cm	**22** 24 cm	**23** 10 604	**24** 6 kg
25 51	**26** 200 kg	**27** 312	**28** 24
29 72	**30** 3170		

Exercise 32B

1 12	**2** 7	**3** 6	**4** 12
5 4	**6** 4	**7** 15	**8** 9
9 16	**10** 7	**11** 9	**12** 15
13 15	**14** 2	**15** 24	**16** 9
17 4	**18** 5	**19** 7	**20** 30
21 20	**22** 45 km/h	**23** 56	**24** 28 cm
25 10.5 cm	**26** 60	**27** $1\frac{1}{3}$	**28** 9 cm
29 70	**30** 26		

33 DIVISION INTO PARTS USING A RATIO

Exercise 33A

1 21, 14	**2** 20, 10
3 64, 48	**4** 240, 160
5 25, 15	**6** 170, 204
7 £2.00, £2.50	**8** 7.5 m, 1.5 m
9 120, 130	**10** £1.30, £5.20
11 15 m, 3 m	**12** £12.60, £21.00
13 £1.53, £10.71	**14** £4.20, £7.80

15 £2.48, £3.72	**16** 28.5 kg, 47.5 kg
17 £9.92, £14.88	**18** £7.12, £14.24, £35.60
19 10.52 g, 13.15 g, 15.78 g	
20 24, 27, 30	
21 3.68 l, 5.52 l, 9.2 l	
22 300, 450, 450	
23 £31.00, £37.20, £62.00	
24 167.4 kg, 223.2 kg, 279 kg	

Exercise 33B

1 120, 80	**2** 40, 20
3 100, 125	**4** 128, 96
5 300, 360	**6** 24p, 56p
7 1.2 kg, 4.8 kg	**8** 72, 36
9 £2.14, £6.42	**10** £2.10, £3.90
11 £11.00, £13.75	**12** £6.48, £8.64
13 3.9 l, 19.5 l	**14** 15.7 m, 31.4 m
15 23.2 kg, 139.2 kg	**16** £3.90, £19.50
17 £9.44, £18.88, £23.60	
18 16p, 64p, 80p	
19 £17.50, £32.50, £40.00	
20 3.45 kg, 13.8 kg, 13.8 kg	
21 5.84 m, 8.76 m, 11.68 m	
22 54, 48, 42	
23 6.3 m, 12.6 m, 15.75 m	
24 8.57 km, 34.28 km, 34.28 km	

R EVISION

Exercise B

1 (a) $\frac{1}{8} = \frac{2}{16} = \frac{3}{24} = \frac{4}{32} = \frac{6}{48}$

   (b) $\frac{7}{12} = \frac{14}{24} = \frac{21}{36} = \frac{35}{60} = \frac{56}{96}$

2 (a) £1.04   (b) 12 kg   (c) £10

3 (a) $\frac{3}{8}$ (b) $\frac{3}{7}$ (c) $\frac{3}{5}$

4 (a) $\frac{13}{4}$ (b) $\frac{24}{5}$ (c) $\frac{25}{3}$

5 (a) $\frac{17}{20}$ (b) $\frac{3}{8}$ (c) $2\frac{13}{20}$ (d) $\frac{63}{100}$

   (e) $\frac{13}{20}$ (f) $\frac{3}{40}$

6 (a) 0.3125   (b) 3.4   (c) 2.175   (d) 0.63

   (e) 0.375   (f) 0.128

7 (a) 7%   (b) $66\frac{1}{2}$%   (c) $103\frac{1}{4}$%   (d) 35%

   (e) $62\frac{1}{2}$%   (f) $81\frac{1}{4}$%

8 (a) $3\frac{1}{4}$ (b) $3\frac{2}{5}$ (c) $5\frac{2}{5}$

9 (a) $1\frac{1}{5}$ (b) $1\frac{3}{8}$ (c) $4\frac{5}{8}$ (d) $2\frac{1}{4}$

   (e) $\frac{9}{16}$ (f) $2\frac{5}{8}$ (g) $2\frac{1}{4}$ (h) $\frac{21}{40}$

   (i) $2\frac{3}{16}$ (j) $\frac{5}{36}$

10 (a) £3.45   (b) 6 kg

11 (a) 65　　　(b) £8　　　(c) £2.50　　　(d) $460

　　(e) 27 cm　(f) 120 ml

12 (a) $\frac{3}{5}$　　　(b) $\frac{3}{25}$

13 (a) $37\frac{1}{2}$%　(b) 56%

14 (a) 3 : 7　　(b) 2 : 9　　　(c) 1 : 6

15 (a) 24p, 56p　　　　(b) £1, £1.50, £2

Exercise BB

1 £7.25

2 112 cm

3 £40.64

4 £357

5 £22.72

6 £101.05

7 £26.38

8 £361.25

9 £10 658.36

10 £176.25

11 2484

12 52%

13 96%

14 $22\frac{1}{2}$%

15 $6\frac{1}{2}$%

16 80p, 20p

17 1.9 kg, 80 g, 20 g

18 2850, 3990, 4560 schillings

Algebra

34 CONTINUING A NUMBER SEQUENCE

Exercise 34A

1 12, 14	**2** 53, 64	**3** 27, 31
4 50, 57	**5** 47, 55	**6** 45, 56
7 33, 39	**8** 44, 35	**9** 25, 18
10 15, 11	**11** 17, 23	**12** 23, 32
13 25, 35	**14** 30, 39	**15** 34, 45
16 35, 49	**17** 43, 60	**18** 51, 83
19 40, 55	**20** 36, 49	**21** 39, 45
22 47, 67	**23** 68, 76	**24** 54, 79
25 74, 82	**26** 31, 43	**27** 57, 80
28 33, 44	**29** 35, 37	**30** 79, 113

Exercise 34B

1 29, 34	**2** 52, 61	**3** 29, 32
4 41, 47	**5** 29, 32	**6** 18, 22
7 37, 44	**8** 59, 54	**9** 8, 5
10 8, 2	**11** 22, 32	**12** 28, 39
13 43, 59	**14** 36, 50	**15** 52, 72
16 58, 83	**17** 61, 82	**18** 53, 76
19 44, 48	**20** 70, 80	**21** 48, 59
22 37, 57	**23** 35, 39	**24** 41, 60
25 52, 71	**26** 56, 77	**27** 70, 78
28 39, 56	**29** 89, 115	**30** 102, 112

35 MAKING PREDICTIONS AND GENERALISING IN A NUMBER SERIES

Exercise 35A

1 + 5; 15, 20	**2** + 8; 18, 28
3 − 2; 13, 18	**4** − 4; 16, 21
5 + 12; 22, 32	**6** − 5; 15, 25
7 $\times 2$, + 1; 31, 41	**8** $\times 2$, + 5; 25, 45
9 $\times 2$, − 4; 16, 36	**10** $\times 3$, + 5; 35, 65
11 $\times 3$, − 2; 28, 43	**12** $\times 4$, + 1; 41, 81
13 $\times 3$, − 5; 40, 55	**14** $\times 5$, − 3; 72, 97
15 $\times 2$, + 9; 39, 59	**16** $\times 4$, + 4; 84, 124
17 $\times 2$, − 1; 29, 59	**18** $\times 3$, − 3; 57, 87
19 $\times 2$, + 6; 36, 46	**20** $\times 2$, − 7; 33; 53
21 $\times 4$, + 6; 66, 106	**22** $\times 4$, − 2; 78, 118
23 $\times 3$, + 6; 66, 96	**24** $\times 5$, − 1; 99, 199
25 $\times 8$, − 1; 159, 319	**26** $\times 5$, + 2; 152, 252
27 $\times 6$, + 3; 123, 303	**28** $\times 3$, + 2; 62, 152

29 Subtract from 20; 10, 5
30 Subtract twice from 30; 10, 0

Exercise 35B

1 + 9; 19, 24	**2** + 4; 14, 24
3 − 1; 9, 19	**4** − 3; 12, 17
5 + 11; 21, 31	**6** − 6; 14, 24
7 $\times 4$, + 2; 62, 82	**8** $\times 2$, + 2; 42, 62
9 $\times 2$, − 6; 24, 34	**10** $\times 3$, + 3; 33, 63
11 $\times 4$, + 3; 43, 63	**12** $\times 3$, − 1; 29, 59
13 $\times 2$, − 2; 28, 38	**14** $\times 2$, + 7; 47, 67
15 $\times 4$, + 2; 82, 122	**16** $\times 3$, − 4; 26, 56
17 $\times 2$, − 3; 27, 47	**18** $\times 5$, + 3; 103, 153
19 $\times 4$, − 1; 59, 79	**20** $\times 5$, − 4; 96, 146
21 $\times 4$, − 4; 56, 96	**22** $\times 4$, + 5; 85, 125
23 $\times 2$, − 1; 39, 59	**24** $\times 5$, + 1; 101, 201
25 $\times 3$, + 4; 64, 124	**26** $\times 7$, − 1; 209, 349
27 $\times 5$, − 2; 98, 248	**28** $\times 6$, + 2; 122, 302

29 Subtract from 25; 15, 10
30 Subtract twice from 40; 20, 10

36 SERIES FROM DIAGRAMS

Exercise 36A

1 $\times 2$	**2** $\times 2$, + 1	**3** $\times 3$, + 1
4 $\times 2$, + 2	**5** $\times 4$	**6** $\times 2$, + 1
7 $\times 2$, + 2	**8** $\times 5$, + 3	**9** $\times 4$, + 4
10 $\times 5$, + 1	**11** $\times 3$, + 2	**12** $\times 2$, − 1
13 $\times 5$, + 1	**14** $\times 4$, + 2	**15** $\times 9$, + 4

Exercise 36B

1 $\times 3$	**2** + 1	**3** $\times 2$, + 2
4 + 2	**5** $\times 5$, + 2	**6** $\times 4$, + 2
7 $\times 2$	**8** − 1	**9** $\times 3$, + 3
10 $\times 7$, + 3	**11** $\times 8$, + 5	**12** $\times 2$, + 4
13 $\times 5$, + 3	**14** $\times 9$, + 2	**15** $\times 2$, − 2

37 COLLECTING LIKE TERMS (1)

Exercise 37A

1 $3x$	**2** $2y$	**3** $4w$
4 d	**5** 0	**6** $3g$
7 $6a$	**8** $5a$	**9** $10d$
10 $9b$	**11** $6y$	**12** $12a$

13 $5c$	**14** $4x$	**15** $6m$			
16 $7a + 6b$	**17** $2a + 2b$	**18** $s + t$			
19 $4b$	**20** $3w + y$	**21** $3a + 6b$			
22 $a + 3b + 4c$	**23** $6m + 9n$	**24** $7y$			
25 $3a + 3b$	**26** $3x + 2y$	**27** $2a + b + c$			
28 $p + 3q$	**29** $2a + 2c$	**30** $5s + 4t$			

Exercise 37B

1 $4a$	**2** $2b$	**3** $3c$
4 $3e$	**5** $3y$	**6** x
7 $3w$	**8** $8c$	**9** $2e$
10 $5a$	**11** $4f$	**12** $8b$
13 $3x$	**14** $12w$	**15** $2x + 3y$
16 $6b + 2c$	**17** $4x + 3y$	**18** $5a$
19 $2x + 4y$	**20** $9a + 2b$	**21** $4a + 5c$
22 $6a + 3x + 7y$	**23** $4s + t$	**24** $3p + 4q$
25 $5x + 5y$	**26** $8a$	**27** $3x + 2y$
28 $5a + 4c$	**29** $a + 3b + 3c$	**30** $a + 5b + 4c$

38 COLLECTING LIKE TERMS (2)

Exercise 38A

1 $4x^2 + 3x$	**2** $cd + 4xy$
3 $28ab$	**4** $5x^2 + x$
5 $11a^3$	**6** $4y^2 + 3x + y$
7 $7x^4 + 10x^3 + 10x^2$	**8** $4x^2y^2$
9 $10a^2y^2 + 2ay^2$	**10** $4a^3 + 2a^2 + 16a$
11 $4xyuv$	**12** $19a^2$
13 $8mn$	**14** $ab + 6b$
15 $6xyw$	**16** $6a^3 + 17a^2$
17 $9abc + 7ab - 2a$	**18** $16xy$
19 $a^5 + 3a^2 + 3a$	**20** $4x^2 - x^3 - 2x^5$
21 $7x^3 - x^2 - 6$	**22** $x^2 + 8x - 3$
23 $4a^3 - a^4 - a$	**24** $9t^4 + 4t^2 + 6$
25 $2pqr^2 + 3pqr$	**26** $4x^3$
27 $3abc + 4$	**28** $4de^2f + 2def$
29 $5a^3 + a^2 + 6a$	**30** $3a^5 + 2a^4 - a^2$

Exercise 38B

1 $4xy + 6y$	**2** $6xy$
3 $2y^2 + 10x + 3y$	**4** $3x^3 + 5x^2$
5 $13x^2 + 3x$	**6** $4a^2y^2 + ay^2$
7 $3cd + d$	**8** $3a^3 + a^2 + 14a$
9 $5abcd$	**10** $5cd^2$
11 $8mn$	**12** $5xy + 5x$
13 $4p^3 + 11p^2$	**14** $8pqr$
15 $a^5 + 3a^2 + a$	**16** $6xy$
17 $7a^2$	**18** $6a^3 + 3a$
19 $x^2 - 2x^3 - 3x^5$	**20** $5pqr - 3pq + 5p$
21 $6x^3 - 2x^4 - 7$	**22** $3a^3 - 2a^4 - a$
23 $2x^2 + 6x - 3$	**24** $a^2bc + 2a^2bc + 3abc$

25 $10t^3 + 6t^2 - 2t$		**26** $5x^3 - 3x^2$	
27 $4stuv$		**28** $2a^3 - a^2 + 6a$	
29 $3a^5 + 5a^4 + a^3 - 2a^2$		**30** $2pq^2r + pqr^2 + 2pqr$	

39 MULTIPLICATION AND DIVISION IN ALGEBRA

Exercise 39A

1 b^2	**2** $4f$	**3** $\dfrac{b}{c}$	**4** gh
5 mn	**6** $\dfrac{x}{y}$	**7** $\dfrac{a}{3}$	**8** $3a$
9 $\dfrac{5}{k}$	**10** $\dfrac{d^2}{e}$	**11** $\dfrac{f}{d^2}$	**12** pqr
13 $3fg$	**14** $5uv$	**15** def	**16** $\dfrac{ab}{4}$
17 $\dfrac{b^2}{c}$	**18** $\dfrac{3j}{k}$	**19** $\dfrac{4}{r}$	**20** $\dfrac{t}{5}$
21 c^2d	**22** $\dfrac{d^2}{f}$	**23** $\dfrac{gh}{i}$	**24** $\dfrac{3c}{2}$
25 $12st$	**26** $4jkl$	**27** $\dfrac{4b}{5}$	**28** $\dfrac{f^2}{g}$
29 $\dfrac{1}{a^2}$	**30** $12t^2$		

Exercise 39B

1 ab	**2** $\dfrac{f}{c}$	**3** $\dfrac{b^2}{d}$	**4** $\dfrac{t}{5}$
5 $\dfrac{7}{q}$	**6** $\dfrac{y}{w}$	**7** $3r^2$	**8** $7t$
9 c^2	**10** ky	**11** mn	**12** cde
13 $4st$	**14** $8k^2$	**15** $3qr$	**16** $\dfrac{g^2}{e}$
17 $\dfrac{ab}{4}$	**18** $\dfrac{9}{q^2}$	**19** $\dfrac{f^2}{h}$	**20** $\dfrac{jm}{3}$
21 $eqrw$	**22** $adfs$	**23** $\dfrac{1}{t}$	**24** $\dfrac{7d}{e}$
25 $5s^2$	**26** $3fgh$	**27** $3f^2g$	**28** y^3
29 $\dfrac{9q}{r}$	**30** $7stu$		

40 MULTIPLYING OUT BRACKETS

Exercise 40A

1 $3x - 3$	**2** $4a - 8$	**3** $2a + 8$
4 $6x - 18$	**5** $5x + 5y$	**6** $2a - 2b$
7 $3x - 3y$	**8** $7a + 7b$	**9** $36 + 6d$
10 $5c + 30$	**11** $6x + 12$	**12** $6x - 8$
13 $10x - 15$	**14** $10x - 15$	**15** $7x + 14$
16 $8x + 12$	**17** $5p + 10q$	**18** $4x + 20$
19 $6x - 4y$	**20** $6x - 15$	**21** $6x - 4$
22 $9x + 12$	**23** $6x - 8$	**24** $16x + 28$

25	$20x - 12$	26	$16x - 12$	27	$4x + 26$
28	$8x + 8y$	29	$9x + 6$	30	$15x - 6$

Exercise 40B

1	$2y - 8$	2	$3r + 9$	3	$5x + 5y$
4	$6a + 6b$	5	$4p + 4q$	6	$3s - 3t$
7	$2p - 2q$	8	$5t + 5s$	9	$4s - 12$
10	$3p + 9$	11	$6x + 27$	12	$4x + 4$
13	$10x + 14$	14	$9x + 6$	15	$20x + 5$
16	$9x + 6$	17	$12x + 24$	18	$21s + 3u$
19	$12m - 30n$	20	$15f - 6e$	21	$24x - 16$
22	$12x + 20$	23	$6x - 3$	24	$4x - 6$
25	$10x - 5$	26	$10x + 2$	27	$18x + 15y$
28	$12x - 4$	29	$15x + 10$	30	$6x + 15y$

41 SIMPLIFYING WITH BRACKETS

Exercise 41A

1	$6m + 8n$	2	$7p + 4q$	3	$14x$
4	$21x + 14y$	5	$9d + 7e$	6	$6m + 24n$
7	$14c + 14d$	8	$5e$	9	$18x + 7y$
10	$d + 3e$	11	$17y$	12	$22q + 8r$
13	$5a + 2b$	14	$9p + q$	15	$5c + 2d$
16	$13x + 2$	17	$2x + 8y$	18	$8x + 18$
19	$8c + 6$	20	$26x + 13$	21	$14b + 11c$
22	$12e - 3f$	23	$2x + 17$	24	$17x - 20$
25	$19 - 10k$	26	$7d + 6$	27	$25y - 46$
28	$22b - 29$	29	$29b - 16a$	30	$2x + 17y$

Exercise 41B

1	$23e + 13f$	2	$10a + 26b$	3	$7p + q$
4	$5y + w$	5	$23s + t$	6	$11p + 4q$
7	$3a + 17b$	8	$26m + 6n$	9	$10g + 37h$
10	$10a + 5b$	11	$2c + 5d$	12	$3x + 9y$
13	$6s + 8t$	14	$15x + 1$	15	$7p + 4q$
16	$13r$	17	$14s + 20$	18	$3p + 6q + 5r$
19	$14x + 27$	20	$8p + 4$	21	$14c$
22	$14x + 11y$	23	$4g + 9h - 2d$	24	$21t - 30$
25	$15m - 20$	26	2	27	$5a - 17$
28	$14 - 9p$	29	$6s + 29t$	30	0

R EVISION

Exercise C

1 (a) $5d$ (b) $6x$ (c) $8f + 6g$ (d) $7y$

(e) $5y^2 + 4y$ (f) $6a^2$ (g) $3pqr^2 + 2pq^2r$

(h) $3d^3 + 5d^2 + 4d$ (i) a^3 (j) $\dfrac{b^2c}{3}$

(k) $3pqr$ (l) $\dfrac{de}{f}$

2 (a) $3x + 6$ (b) $12x - 8$ (c) $10d - 5e$

(d) $18f + 30g$ (e) $16x + 21y$ (f) $5c$

(g) $5t - 6$ (h) $10m + 16n$

Exercise CC

1 (a) 36, 44   (b) 8, 5   (c) 27, 37

(d) 18, 27   (e) 39, 54   (f) 36, 51

2 (a) (i) x 3, + 1 (ii) 31, 61

(b) (i) x 2, – 2 (ii) 18, 38

(c) (i) + 6 (ii) 16, 26

(d) (i) x 3, – 3 (ii) 27, 57

(e) (i) x 4, – 3 (ii) 37, 77

(f) (i) Subtract from 30 (ii) 20, 10

(g) (i) x 3, + 2 (ii) 32, 62

(h) (i) x 2, + 3 (ii) 23, 43

42 SOLVING SIMPLE EQUATIONS (1)

Exercise 42A

1	3	2	2	3	9	4	8	5	4
6	7	7	9	8	8	9	6	10	4
11	9	12	12	13	14	14	19	15	17
16	18	17	16	18	22	19	18	20	17
21	18	22	15	23	8	24	20	25	7
26	12	27	18	28	5	29	14	30	9

Exercise 42B

1	4	2	7	3	6	4	5	5	3
6	8	7	8	8	7	9	2	10	4
11	9	12	18	13	17	14	14	15	18
16	15	17	12	18	21	19	15	20	17
21	14	22	17	23	22	24	12	25	10
26	9	27	6	28	13	29	8	30	7

43 SOLVING SIMPLE EQUATIONS (2)

Exercise 43A

1	6	2	2	3	3	4	6	5	9
6	28	7	2	8	5	9	9	10	7
11	32	12	45	13	56	14	5	15	12
16	2	17	27	18	42	19	6	20	8
21	7	22	4	23	35	24	19	25	7
26	15	27	1	28	40	29	0	30	28

Exercise 43B

1	5	2	4	3	2	4	6	5	20
6	6	7	5	8	3	9	21	10	4
11	36	12	2	13	8	14	1	15	8
16	18	17	1	18	56	19	14	20	9

21 6 **22** 35 **23** 1 **24** 24 **25** 11
26 32 **27** 24 **28** 2 **29** 15 **30** 3

44 SOLVING HARDER EQUATIONS

Exercise 44A

1 2	**2** 3	**3** 5	**4** 7	**5** 2
6 7	**7** 9	**8** 3	**9** 1	**10** 2
11 8	**12** 2	**13** 5	**14** 1	**15** 5
16 7	**17** 9	**18** 1	**19** 3	**20** 4
21 6	**22** 7	**23** 2	**24** 5	**25** 4
26 9	**27** 7	**28** 8	**29** 6	**30** 2

Exercise 44B

1 7	**2** 8	**3** 5	**4** 4	**5** 5
6 2	**7** 1	**8** 5	**9** 7	**10** 4
11 7	**12** 3	**13** 2	**14** 1	**15** 8
16 7	**17** 5	**18** 6	**19** 2	**20** 6
21 9	**22** 3	**23** 9	**24** 7	**25** 3
26 8	**27** 7	**28** 9	**29** 6	**30** 4

45 EQUATIONS WITH BRACKETS

Exercise 45A

1 3	**2** 6	**3** 5	**4** 6	**5** 3
6 2	**7** 3	**8** 4	**9** 5	**10** 2
11 6	**12** 1	**13** 2	**14** 4	**15** 5
16 8	**17** 6	**18** 3	**19** 4	**20** 3
21 2	**22** 7	**23** 4	**24** 6	**25** 9
26 2	**27** 8	**28** 7	**29** 2	**30** 9

Exercise 45B

1 2	**2** 4	**3** 1	**4** 4	**5** 6
6 5	**7** 2	**8** 1	**9** 6	**10** 8
11 7	**12** 5	**13** 6	**14** 7	**15** 3
16 4	**17** 2	**18** 3	**19** 4	**20** 5
21 3	**22** 2	**23** 4	**24** 8	**25** 3
26 9	**27** 5	**28** 9	**29** 2	**30** 6

46 SUBSTITUTION

Exercise 46A

1 6	**2** 12	**3** 20	**4** 7	**5** 8
6 1	**7** 12	**8** 2	**9** 20	**10** 8
11 8	**12** 18	**13** 6	**14** 18	**15** 9
16 6	**17** 25	**18** 7	**19** 16	**20** 48

Exercise 46B

1 9	**2** 8	**3** 10	**4** 40	**5** 45
6 7	**7** 7	**8** 15	**9** 22	**10** 21
11 16	**12** 12	**13** 6	**14** 25	**15** 6
16 2	**17** 6	**18** 7	**19** 35	**20** 24

Exercise 46C

1 (a) 11 (b) 13		**2** (a) 18 (b) 11	
3 (a) 6 (b) 0		**4** (a) 26 (b) 27	
5 (a) 0 (b) 10		**6** (a) 14 (b) 38	
7 (a) 55 (b) 61		**8** (a) 36 (b) 27	
9 (a) 5 (b) 6		**10** (a) 7 (b) 5	
11 (a) 20 (b) 42		**12** (a) 2 (b) 3.5	
13 (a) 14 (b) 25		**14** (a) 2 (b) 13.5	
15 (a) 13 (b) 17		**16** (a) 21 (b) 39	
17 (a) 44 (b) 52		**18** (a) 8 (b) 5.5	
19 (a) 8 (b) 15		**20** (a) 18 (b) 98	

Exercise 46D

1 (a) 32 (b) 40		**2** (a) 1 (b) 17	
3 (a) 4 (b) 21		**4** (a) 23 (b) 30	
5 (a) 25 (b) 16		**6** (a) 16 (b) 22	
7 (a) 42 (b) 47		**8** (a) 18 (b) 3	
9 (a) 30 (b) 18		**10** (a) 5 (b) 21	
11 (a) 14 (b) 20		**12** (a) 40 (b) 48	
13 (a) 9 (b) 31		**14** (a) 6 (b) 13	
15 (a) 4 (b) 4		**16** (a) 9 (b) 0	
17 (a) 3 (b) 0.5		**18** (a) 15 (b) 0	
19 (a) 1.5 (b) 27		**20** (a) 25 (b) 313	

47 WRITING ALGEBRAIC EXPRESSIONS

Exercise 47A

1 $x + 8$	**2** $d - 7$	**3** $8k$
4 $\dfrac{5}{f}$	**5** $3g$	**6** $c - 6$
7 $\dfrac{p}{q}$	**8** $s + t$	**9** ab
10 $\dfrac{j}{9}$	**11** $3r$	**12** $b + 18$
13 $x + y$	**14** $s - v$	**15** $t + 4$
16 $100d$ metres	**17** $5b$ pence	**18** $200x$ pence
19 £$(m - n)$	**20** $2t$ pence	**21** $w - v$ cm
22 $60t$ seconds	**23** $48 - w$	**24** $f + s$ pence
25 $T + W$ tonnes	**26** £cn	**27** $24d$ hours
28 £$(p + q + r)$	**29** £$4h$	**30** ng grams

Exercise 47B

1 $10 + y$	**2** $f - 6$	**3** $\dfrac{7}{m}$
4 ef	**5** $q - 4$	**6** $4 - q$

7 $s + t$ **8** $\dfrac{x}{3}$ **9** $t + 15$

10 $g + h$ **11** $\dfrac{10}{d}$ **12** $n + 4$

13 $\dfrac{1}{y}$ **14** $3h$ **15** $n - m$

16 $100x$ pence   **17** $1000f$ grams   **18** $5m$ pence
19 $12y$ pence   **20** $m - n$ **21** $x + y$ pence
22 $y + 18$ years   **23** $T - 3$ **24** $g + b$
25 $p - 3$ **26** £gn **27** $K - T$ metres
28 $60h$ min   **29** $40 + x$ years   **30** $n + 1$

48 WRITING EQUATIONS

Exercise 48A

1 $2x + 8 = 26$; 9   **2** $3x - 4 = 29$; 11
3 $2x + 7 = 17$; 5   **4** $4x - 8 = 20$; 7
5 $3x + 6 = 21$; 5   **6** $3(x + 5) = 39$; 8
7 $4x + 2 = 10$; 2   **8** $3x - 8 = 10$; 6
9 $2x - 4 = 2$; 3   **10** $4x - 2 = 10$; 3
11 $2x + 12 = 20$; £4   **12** $3x = 42$; 14 km
13 $2x + 18 = 82$; 32   **14** $2x + 21 = 91$; 56
15 $\dfrac{4x}{3} = 436$; £327   **16** $6x = 126$; £21
17 $8x = 32$; 4   **18** $3x - 2 = 37$; 13
19 $3x - 9 = 18$; 9   **20** $3x + 64 = 103$; 13
21 24°   **22** 75°   **23** 45°   **24** 70°
25 70°   **26** 20°   **27** 35°   **28** 30°
29 5   **30** 7

Exercise 48B

1 $3x - 5 = 7$; 4   **2** $2x - 6 = 12$; 9
3 $3x + 7 = 28$; 7   **4** $2x + 9 = 25$; 8
5 $2(x + 6) = 18$; 3   **6** $7x + 2 = 16$; 2
7 $2x + 5 = 9$; 2   **8** $6x - 1 = 29$; 5
9 $6x + 3 = 15$; 2   **10** $7x + 4 = 25$; 3
11 $2x + 3.50 = 14.50$; £5.50
12 $240 + x = 275$; 35
13 $4x + 48$; 12   **14** $\dfrac{3x}{2} = 15$; 10
15 $2x + 14 = 82$; £34   **16** $3x + 1 = 43$; 14
17 $2x + 10 = 24$; 7   **18** $2x + 9 = 31$; 11 m
19 $4x + 20 = 80$; 15p   **20** $4x + 6 = 42$; £9
21 30°   **22** 70°   **23** 60°   **24** 40°
25 70°   **26** 45°   **27** 25°   **28** 50°
29 5   **30** 7

49 TRIAL AND IMPROVEMENT

Exercise 49A

1 3.83, –1.83   **2** 1.45, –3.45

3 3.30, –0.30   **4** –5.16, 1.16
5 –3.88, 0.38   **6** 2.35
7 –0.29, –1.71   **8** 13.78, 0.22
9 1.59, –1.26   **10** 4.67, 0.32
11 1.18, –0.85   **12** 2.56, –1.56
13 2.15   **14** 0.7, –2.7
15 1.58   **16** –0.38, –2.62
17 2.08   **18** –1.76, –0.56
19 2.64, 0.75   **20** –3.11, –0.21

Exercise 49B

1 1.16, –5.16   **2** 1.62, –0.62
3 4.47, –4.47   **4** 3.19, 0.31
5 2.84, 0.81   **6** 3.91
7 2.19, –0.69   **8** 1.43, 0.23
9 1.41, 0.30   **10** 1.81
11 3.64, –0.14   **12** 2.16, –0.36
13 –4.23, 0.23   **14** 6.46, –0.46
15 10.18, –1.18   **16** 7.69, –0.19
17 1.91   **18** 3.69, –0.36
19 –3.34, 0.59   **20** –3.58, –0.41

50 DRAWING AND INTERPRETING CONVERSION GRAPHS

Exercise 50A

1 (a) 2.8 t, 6.4 t, 3.8 t, 8.4 t
  (b) 21 200 lb, 16 400 lb, 9200 lb, 19 400 lb
2 (a) £1.60, £6.40, £8.80, £3.40
  (b) 1360 pta, 760 pta, 500 pta, 1100 pta
3

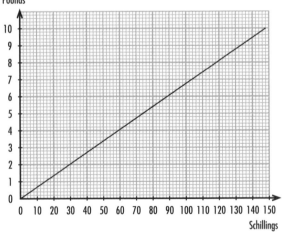

(a) £2.00, £3.80, £8.10, £6.60
(b) 89 schillings, 37 schillings, 139 schillings, 112 schillings

4

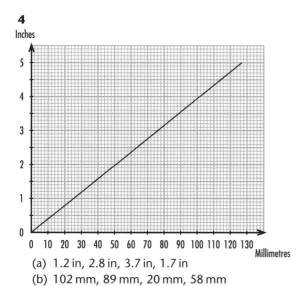

(a) 1.2 in, 2.8 in, 3.7 in, 1.7 in
(b) 102 mm, 89 mm, 20 mm, 58 mm

5

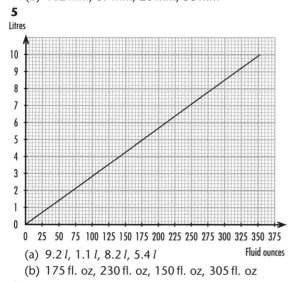

(a) 9.2 *l*, 1.1 *l*, 8.2 *l*, 5.4 *l*
(b) 175 fl. oz, 230 fl. oz, 150 fl. oz, 305 fl. oz

6

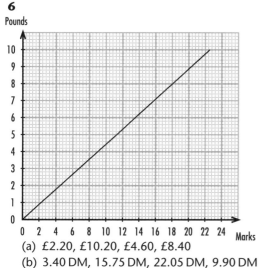

(a) £2.20, £10.20, £4.60, £8.40
(b) 3.40 DM, 15.75 DM, 22.05 DM, 9.90 DM

7

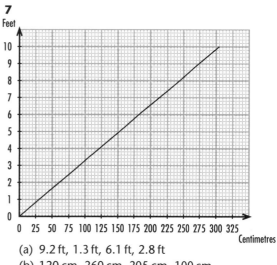

(a) 9.2 ft, 1.3 ft, 6.1 ft, 2.8 ft
(b) 120 cm, 260 cm, 205 cm, 100 cm

8

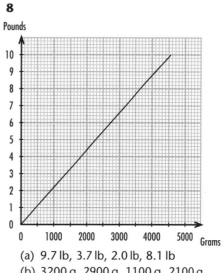

(a) 9.7 lb, 3.7 lb, 2.0 lb, 8.1 lb
(b) 3200 g, 2900 g, 1100 g, 2100 g

Exercise 50B

1 (a) 2.8 oz, 7.0 oz, 4.4 oz, 8.8 oz
 (b) 114 g, 226 g, 182 g, 102 g

2 (a) 1.8 cu. ft, 5.6 cu. ft, cu. ft, 7.4 cu. ft
 (b) 55 000 cm^3, 265 000 cm^3, 175 000 cm^3, 100 000 cm^3

3

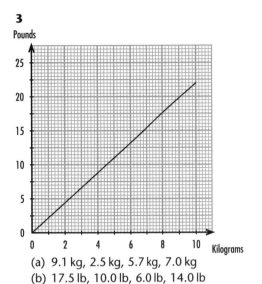

Pounds / Kilograms

(a) 9.1 kg, 2.5 kg, 5.7 kg, 7.0 kg
(b) 17.5 lb, 10.0 lb, 6.0 lb, 14.0 lb

4

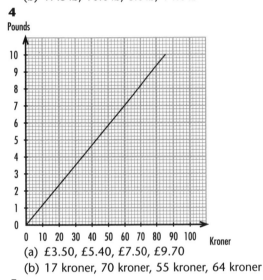

Pounds / Kroner

(a) £3.50, £5.40, £7.50, £9.70
(b) 17 kroner, 70 kroner, 55 kroner, 64 kroner

5

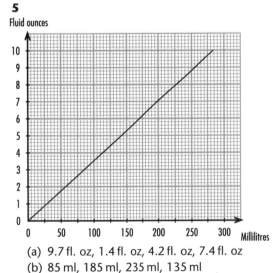

Fluid ounces / Millilitres

(a) 9.7 fl. oz, 1.4 fl. oz, 4.2 fl. oz, 7.4 fl. oz
(b) 85 ml, 185 ml, 235 ml, 135 ml

6

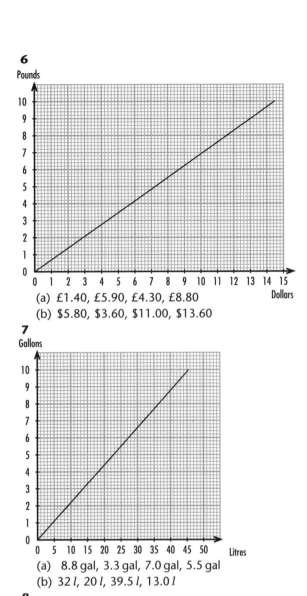

Pounds / Dollars

(a) £1.40, £5.90, £4.30, £8.80
(b) $5.80, $3.60, $11.00, $13.60

7

Gallons / Litres

(a) 8.8 gal, 3.3 gal, 7.0 gal, 5.5 gal
(b) 32 *l*, 20 *l*, 39.5 *l*, 13.0 *l*

8

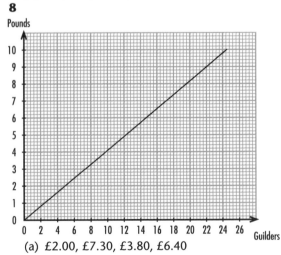

Pounds / Guilders

(a) £2.00, £7.30, £3.80, £6.40
(b) 7.50 guilders, 11.00 guilders,
    21.00 guilders, 13.00 guilders

51 READING POINTS IN ALL FOUR QUADRANTS

Exercise 51A

1 A = (−4, 4), B = (2, 1), C = (0, 3), D = (4, −4),
E = (0, −5), F = (5, 4), G = (−2, −2)

2 I = (−4,5), J = (0, 2), K = (4, 4), L = (−3, 1),
M = (2, −5), N = (4, −4), P = (2, 0),
Q = (−3, −3)

3 R = (−3, 6), S = (−5, 1), T = (3, −4), U = (3, 0),
V = (5, 4), W = (−2, −2), X = (−4, −3), Y = (0, 4)

4 A = (−1, 5), B = (5, −3), C = (2, 0), D = (−2, 3),
E = (−3, −2), F = (0, 3), G = (5, 4), H = (−1, −4)

5 I = (−5, 2), J = (−2, 3), K = (0, 6), L = (−4, −4),
M = (3, −5), N = (5, −2), P = (3, 4), Q = (4, 0)

6 R = (−4, 4), S = (−5, 1), T = (5, 2), U = (0, 2),
V = (1, −2), W = (4, −3), X = (−1, 0), Y = (−5, −5)

Exercise 51B

1 A = (−3, 3), B = (−2, 1), C = (3, 5), D = (3, −3),
E = (−5, −4), F = (4, 2), G = (0, −4), H = (5, 0)

2 I = (−2, 5), J = (−4, 2), K = (5, −4), L = (0, −3),
M = (4, 2), N = (1, 0), P = (−5, −4),
Q = (−2, −1)

3 R = (−3, 4), S = (−5, 1), T = (3, 1), U = (5, 4),
V = (0, 1), W = (−1, 0), X = (−3, −5), Y = (3, −3)

4 A = (4, 4), B = (1, −4), C = (−1, −5),
D = (−2, 2), E = (2, 0), F = (−5, −2), G = (−4, 1),
H = (5, −3)

5 I = (6, 4), J = (−1, 1), K = (4, 0), L = (1, −3),
M = (4, −4), N = (−2, 5), P = (−5, 3),
Q = (−5, −5)

6 R = (−3, 5), S = (1, 4), T = (−4, −5),
U = (−2, −2), V = (1, −4), W = (4, −3),
X = (5, 1), Y = (−5, 0)

52 PLOTTING POINTS IN ALL FOUR QUADRANTS

Exercise 52A

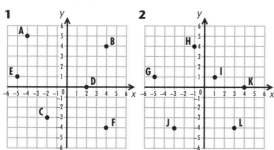

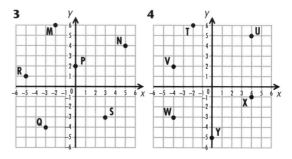

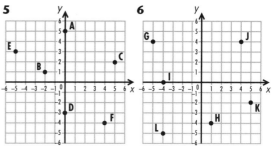

Exercise 52B

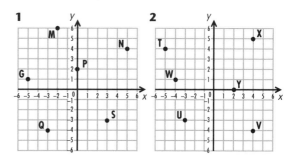

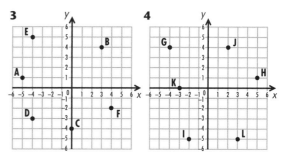

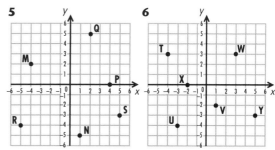

Exercise 52C

1

2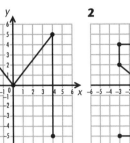

5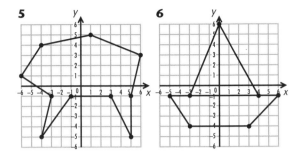

6

3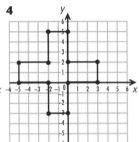

4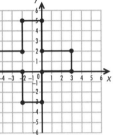

53 DRAWING GRAPHS

Exercise 53A

1 (a)

x	−3	−2	−1	0	1	2	3
y = x − 2	−5	−4	−3	−2	−1	0	1

(b)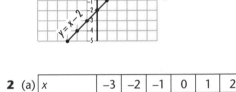

5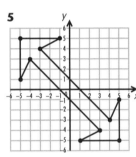

6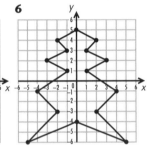

2 (a)

x	−3	−2	−1	0	1	2	3
y = 2x + 2	−4	−2	0	2	4	6	8

(b)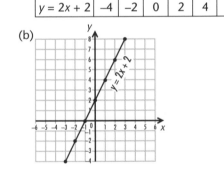

Exercise 52D

1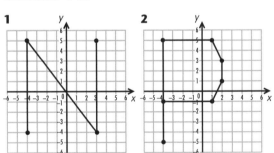

2

3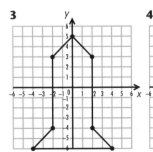

4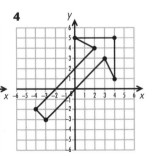

3 (a)

x	−3	−2	−1	0	1	2	3
y = 3x	−9	−6	−3	0	3	6	9

(b)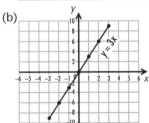

22 ALGEBRA

4 (a)

x	−2	−1	0	1	2	3	4
$y = 4x - 5$	−13	−9	−5	−1	3	7	11

(b)

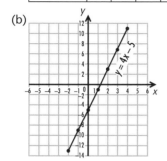

5 (a)

x	−2	−1	0	1	2	3	4
$y = 2x + 3$	−1	1	3	5	7	9	11

(b)

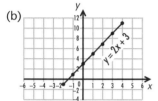

6 (a)

x	−3	−2	−1	0	1	2	3
$y = -2x$	6	4	2	0	−2	−4	−6

(b)

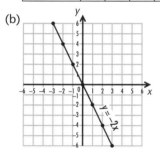

7 (a)

x	−3	−2	−1	0	1	2	3
$y = 2x + 6$	0	2	4	6	8	10	12

(b)

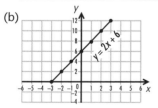

8 (a)

x	−3	−2	−1	0	1	2	3
$y = 2x - 2$	−8	−6	−4	−2	0	2	4

(b)

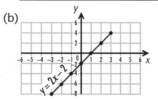

9 (a)

x	−3	−2	−1	0	1	2	3	4
$y = 3x - 2$	−11	−8	−5	−2	1	4	7	10

(b)

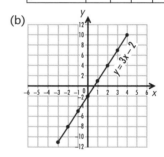

10 (a)

x	−2	−1	0	1	2	3	4
$y = -x$	2	1	0	−1	−2	−3	−4

(b)

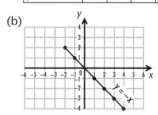

11 (a)

x	−2	−1	0	1	2	3
$y = 4x - 2$	−10	−6	−2	2	6	10

(b)

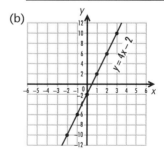

12 (a)

x	−2	−1	0	1	2	3	4
y = 10 − x	12	11	10	9	8	7	6

(b)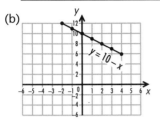

13 (a)

x	−2	−1	0	1	2	3	4
y = 6 − 2x	10	8	6	4	2	0	−2

(b)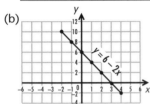

14 (a)

x	−2	−1	0	1	2	3	4
y = 2 − x	4	3	2	1	0	−1	−2

(b)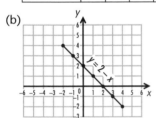

15 (a)

x	−2	0	2	4	6	8	10
y = ½x − 3	−4	−3	−2	−1	0	1	2

(b)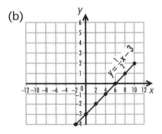

Exercise 53B

1 (a)

x	−3	−2	−1	0	1	2
y = x + 3	0	1	2	3	4	5

(b)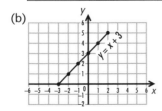

2 (a)

x	−2	−1	0	1	2	3	4
y = 2x + 4	0	2	4	6	8	10	12

(b)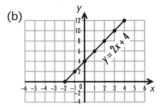

3 (a)

x	−2	−1	0	1	2	3	4
y = x − 1	−3	−2	−1	0	1	2	3

(b)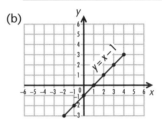

4 (a)

x	−2	−1	0	1	2	3
y = 3x − 4	−10	−7	−4	−1	2	5

(b)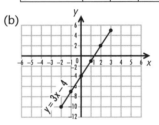

5 (a)

x	−2	−1	0	1	2	3
y = 3x + 2	−4	−1	2	5	8	11

(b)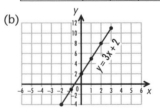

6 (a)

x	−2	−1	0	1	2	3	4
y = 2x − 1	−5	−3	−1	1	3	5	7

(b)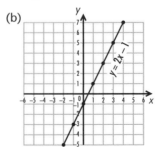

7 (a)

x	−3	−2	−1	0	1	2	3
$y = 2x$	−6	−4	−2	0	2	4	6

(b)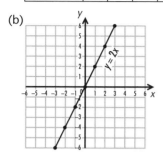

8 (a)

x	−2	−1	0	1	2	3
$y = 3x - 1$	−7	−4	−1	2	5	8

(b)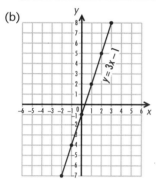

9 (a)

x	−2	−1	0	1	2	3	4
$y = 2x - 3$	−7	−5	−3	−1	1	3	5

(b)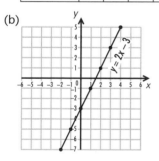

10 (a)

x	−2	−1	0	1	2	3	4
$y = 8 - x$	10	9	8	7	6	5	4

(b)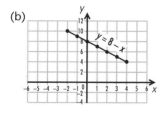

11 (a)

x	−1	0	1	2	3	4	5	6
$y = 12 - 2x$	14	12	10	8	6	4	2	0

(b)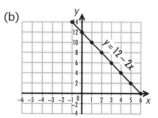

12 (a)

x	−2	−1	0	1	2	3	4
$y = 4 - x$	6	5	4	3	2	1	0

(b)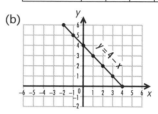

13 (a)

x	−1	0	1	2	3	4	5
$y = 14 - 3x$	17	14	11	8	5	2	−1

(b)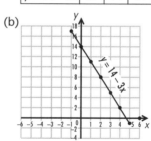

14 (a)

x	−2	−1	0	1	2	3	4
$y = 4x - 1$	−9	−5	−1	3	7	11	15

(b)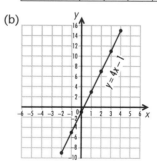

15 (a)

x	−6	−4	−2	0	2	4	6
$y = \frac{1}{2}x + 2$	−1	0	1	2	3	4	5

(b)
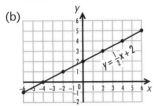

25 (a)

x	−2	−1	0	1	2	3
$y = 4x − 3$	−11	−7	−3	1	5	9

(b)
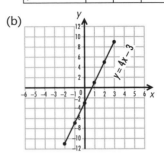

ʀEVISION

Exercise ⅅ

1 9
2 7
3 12
4 8
5 9
6 28
7 1
8 48
9 6
10 9
11 7
12 8
13 8
14 2
15 3
16 4
17 (a) 25　　(b) 1　　(c) 6　　(d) 13
18 (a) 48　　(b) 147
19 (a) 16　　(b) 14
20 (a) 10　　(b) 26
21 (a) 56　　(b) 60
22 (a) 18.34, −16.34　(b) 1.82
23 A = (3, 2), B = (−3, 4), C = (0, −5),
　　D = (−4, −2), E = (1, −3), F = (2, −2)

24
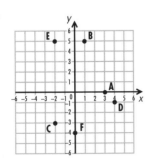

Exercise ⅅⅅ

1 (a) (i) 2x + 3 = 11　(ii) x = 4
　　(b) (i) 20 − 3x = 11　(ii) x = 3
　　(c) (i) 4x = 100　(ii) x = 25 kg
　　(d) (i) 7x = 35　(ii) x = £5
　　(e) (i) 3x + 210 = 360　(ii) x = 50°
　　(f) (i) 3x + 30 = 180　(ii) x = 50°

2 (a) gh　　(b) t − 4　　(c) $\frac{x}{5}$　　(d) d + 7

3 (a) 5c pence　(b) 1000x mm　(c) 40 + y years

4

Square inches
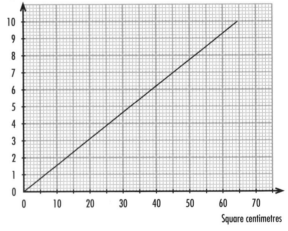
Square centimetres

(a) 9.0 sq. in, 1.7 sq. in, 5.1 sq. in, 3.5 sq. in
(b) 51.5 cm², 15.5 cm², 42.0 cm², 23.0 cm²

Shape, space and measures

54 MEASURING AND IDENTIFYING ANGLES

Exercise 54A

1 Acute 20°		**2** Acute 50°	
3 Acute 70°		**4** Obtuse 110°	
5 Acute 30°		**6** Acute 45°	
7 Obtuse 175°		**8** Acute 85°	
9 Obtuse 150°		**10** Reflex 210°	
11 Reflex 300°		**12** Obtuse 135°	

Exercise 54B

1 Acute 30°		**2** Right 90°	
3 Acute 40°		**4** Acute 80	
5 Obtuse 160°		**6** Obtuse 120°	
7 Acute 65°		**8** Obtuse 95°	
9 Obtuse 125°		**10** Reflex 215°	
11 Obtuse 153°		**12** Acute 60°	

55 DRAWING ANGLES

Exercise 55A

1 Acute	**2** Acute	**3** Acute
4 Acute	**5** Obtuse	**6** Acute
7 Acute	**8** Obtuse	**9** Acute
10 Obtuse	**11** Reflex	**12** Obtuse
13 Reflex	**14** Acute	**15** Reflex
16 Reflex	**17** Obtuse	**18** Reflex
19 Obtuse	**20** Obtuse	**21** Acute
22 Reflex	**23** Obtuse	**24** Reflex
25 Obtuse	**26** Reflex	**27** Straight line
28 Reflex	**29** Obtuse	**30** Reflex

Exercise 55B

1 Acute	**2** Acute	**3** Acute
4 Right	**5** Acute	**6** Acute
7 Obtuse	**8** Obtuse	**9** Reflex
10 Reflex	**11** Reflex	**12** Obtuse
13 Acute	**14** Obtuse	**15** Acute
16 Obtuse	**17** Reflex	**18** Reflex
19 Reflex	**20** Reflex	**21** Obtuse
22 Acute	**23** Obtuse	**24** Reflex
25 Reflex	**26** Reflex	**27** Acute
28 Reflex	**29** Obtuse	**30** Reflex

56 ANGLES AT A POINT AND ON A STRAIGHT LINE

Exercise 56A

1 $a = 93°$		**2** $b = 58°$	
3 $c = 95°$		**4** $d = 145°$	
5 $e = 142°, f = 63°$		**6** $g = 119°$	
7 $h = 49°$		**8** $i = 58°$	
9 $j = 139°$		**10** $k = 38°$	
11 $l = 70°$		**12** $m = 75°$	

Exercise 56B

1 $a = 137°$		**2** $b = 97°$	
3 $c = 45°$		**4** $d = 67°$	
5 $e = 118°, f = 65°$		**6** $g = 150°$	
7 $h = 23°$		**8** $i = 212°$	
9 $j = 49°$		**10** $k = 156°$	
11 $l = 103°$		**12** $m = 51°$	

57 FINDING THE UNKNOWN ANGLE IN A TRIANGLE

Exercise 57A

1 $a = 61°$		**2** $b = 61°$	
3 $c = 85°$		**4** $d = 61°$	
5 $e = 71°$		**6** $f = 107°$	
7 $g = 50°$		**8** $h = 72°$	
9 $i = 48°$		**10** $j = 75°, k = 30°$	
11 $l = 39°$		**12** $m = 31°, n = 31°$	

Exercise 57B

1 $a = 75°$		**2** $b = 138°$	
3 $c = 40°$		**4** $d = 39°$	
5 $e = 58°$		**6** $f = 89°$	
7 $g = 57°$		**8** $h = 102°$	
9 $i = 18°$		**10** $j = 38°, k = 71°$	
11 $l = 34°, m = 34°$		**12** $n = 45°, p = 45°$	

58 SUM OF THE ANGLES IN A QUADRILATERAL

Exercise 58A

1 $a = 63°$		**2** $b = 55°$	
3 $c = 141°$		**4** $d = 32°$	
5 $e = 141°$		**6** $f = 58°$	

7 $g = 162°$ **8** $h = 69°$
9 $i = 121°$ **10** $j = 112°$
11 $k = 45°$ **12** $l = 105°$

Exercise 58B

1 $a = 129°$ **2** $b = 69°$
3 $c = 39°$ **4** $d = 96°$
5 $e = 88°$ **6** $f = 117°$
7 $g = 81°$ **8** $h = 108°$
9 $i = 241°$ **10** $j = 62°$
11 $k = 119°$ **12** $l = 86°$

59 ANGLES ON PARALLEL LINES

Exercise 59A

1 $a = 67°$ (vert. opp.), $b = 67°$ (corresponding)
2 $c = 58°$ (vert. opp.), $d = 122°$ (supplementary),
$e = 58°$ (alternate)
3 $f = 65°$ (supplementary),
$g = 115°$ (corresponding), $h = 115°$ (alternate),
$i = 115°$ (vert. opp.)
4 $j = 85°$ (alternate), $k = 85°$ (corresponding),
$l = 85°$ (vert. opp.)
5 $m = 123°$ (vert. opp.), $n = 123°$ (alternate),
$p = 123°$ (corresponding),
$q = 57°$ (supplementary)
6 $r = 49°$ (corresponding), $s = 49°$ (vert. opp.),
$t = 131°$ (angles on a straight line)
7 $a = 72°$ (corresponding), $b = 72°$ (vert. opp.),
$c = 73°$ (corresponding), $d = 73°$ (vert. opp.)
8 $e = 79°$ (supplementary), $f = 79°$ (supplementary),
$g = 101°$ (corresponding), $h = 101°$ (alternate),
$i = 101°$ (corresponding)
9 $j = 49°$ (vert. opp.), $k = 49°$ (alternate),
$l = 50°$ (vert. opp.), $m = 50°$ (alternate),
$n = 130°$ (supplementary)
10 $p = 48°$ (supplementary),
$q = 132°$ (corresponding),
$r = 132°$ (corresponding),
$s = 48°$ (supplementary), $t = 132°$ (vert. opp.),
$u = 132°$ (alternate)

Exercise 59B

1 $a = 52°$ (alternate), $b = 52°$ (corresponding),
$c = 128°$ (supplementary), $d = 52°$ (vert. opp.)
2 $e = 61°$ (vert. opp.), $f = 61°$ (corresponding)
3 $g = 98°$ (vert. opp.), $h = 98°$ (corresponding)
4 $i = 101°$ (vert. opp.), $j = 79°$ (supplementary),
$k = 101°$ (corresponding), $l = 101°$ (alternate)
5 $m = 49°$ (alternate), $n = 49°$ (corresponding),
$p = 49°$ (vert. opp.)

6 $q = 78°$ (vert. opp.), $r = 78°$ (corresponding)
7 $s = 67°$ (supplementary),
$t = 113°$ (corresponding),
$u = 113°$ (corresponding),
$v = 67°$ (supplementary), $w = 113°$ (vert. opp.)
8 $x = 97°$ (corresponding), $y = 83°$ (supplementary),
$a = 81°$ (vert. opp.), $b = 99°$ (supplementary),
$c = 81°$ (corresponding), $d = 81°$ (alternate)
9 $e = 88°$ (vert. opp.), $f = 88°$ (corresponding),
$g = 88°$ (corresponding), $h = 92°$ (supplementary)
10 $i = 75°$ (corresponding), $j = 75°$ (vert. opp.),
$k = 75°$ (alternate), $l = 88°$ (supplementary),
$m = 92°$ (corresponding), $n = 92°$ (alternate),
$p = 92°$ (vert. opp.)

60 RECOGNISING TRIANGLES, QUADRILATERALS AND POLYGONS

Exercise 60A

1 Isosceles trapezium   **2** Kite
3 Heptagon   **4** Equilateral triangle
5 Rectangle   **6** Parallelogram
7 Square   **8** Rhombus
9 Hexagon   **10** Arrowhead
11 Isosceles triangle   **12** Right-angled triangle

Exercise 60B

1 Pentagon   **2** Square
3 Scalene triangle   **4** Parallelogram
5 Kite   **6** Octagon
7 Rectangle   **8** Rhombus
9 Trapezium   **10** Isosceles triangle
11 Hexagon   **12** Isosceles trapezium

Exercise 60C

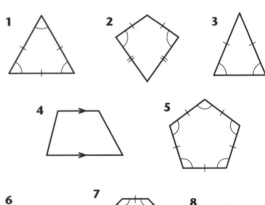

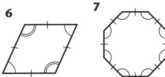

9 Rhombus   **10** Isosceles triangle
11 Isosceles trapezium   **12** Pentagon
13 Yes   **14** Right angle(s)
15 Parallelogram

Exercise 60D

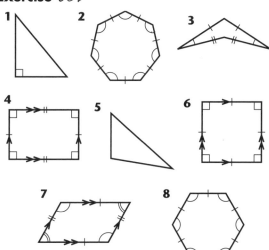

9 Scalene triangle   **10** Trapezium
11 Arrowhead   **12** Hexagon
13 Yes   **14** Rectangle
15 All sides are the same length.

61 ANGLES OF A REGULAR POLYGON

Exercise 61A

1 $a = 60°$, $b = 60°$, $c = 120°$
2 $d = 30°$, $e = 150°$, $f = 30°$
3 $g = 108°$, $h = 72°$, $i = 72°$
4 $j = 128.57°$, $k = 51.43°$, $l = 51.43°$
5 (a) $72°$ (b) $108°$ (c) $72°$
6 18, $160°$
7 $45°$, 8
8 (a) $24°$ (b) $156°$ (c) $25°$
9 $36°$, 10
10 (a) $18°$ (b) $162°$ (c) $18°$

Exercise 61B

1 $a = 135°$, $b = 45°$, $c = 45°$
2 $d = 36°$, $e = 36°$, $f = 144°$
3 $g = 140°$, $h = 40°$, $i = 40°$
4 $j = 156°$, $k = 24°$, $l = 24°$
5 24, $165°$
6 (a) $45°$ (b) $135°$ (c) $45°$
7 $72°$, 5
8 (a) $30°$ (b) $150°$ (c) $30°$

9 $60°$, 6
10 (a) $20°$ (b) $160°$ (c) $20°$

62 FINDING UNKNOWN ANGLES IN VARIOUS SITUATIONS, WITH REASONS

Exercise 62A

1 $a = 44°$ (angles on a straight line)
2 $b = 71°$ (alternate angles),
$c = 71°$ (corresponding angles),
$d = 71°$ (vert. opp. angles)
3 $e = 89°$ (angles of a quadrilateral),
$f = 91°$ (angles on a straight line)
4 $g = 72°$ (angles at centre of a polygon),
$h = 108°$ (int. angles of a polygon),
$i = 72°$ (ext. angles of a polygon)
5 $j = 43°$ (angles on a straight line),
$k = 59°$ (angles on a straight line)
6 $l = 68°$ (angles on a straight line),
$m = 51°$ (angles in a triangle)
7 $n = 39°$ (alternate angles), $p = 56°$ (angles in a triangle), $q = 21°$ (angles in a triangle)
8 $r = 45°$ (angles on a straight line)
9 $s = 50°$ (symmetry), $t = 80°$ (angles of a quadrilateral), $u = 90°$ (symmetry)
10 $v = 72°$ (angles in a triangle), $w = 51°$ (angles in a triangle), $x = 129°$ (angles on a straight line)
11 $a = 56°$ (vert. opp. angles),
$b = 56°$ (corresponding angles),
$c = 124°$ (supplementary angles),
$d = 56°$ (supplementary with c or corresponding with b)
12 $e = 118°$ (alternate angles), $f = 62°$ (angles on a straight line or supplementary),
$g = 28°$ (angles on a straight line),
$h = 62°$ (angles on a straight line)

Exercise 62B

1 $a = 38°$ (angles of a quadrilateral)
2 $b = 123°$ (angles on a straight line),
$c = 71°$ (angles in a triangle),
$d = 109°$ (angles on a straight line)
3 $e = 87°$ (alternate angles),
$f = 93°$ (supplementary angles),
$g = 87°$ (vert. opp. angles),
$h = 87°$ (corresponding angles)
4 $i = 120°$ (int. angles of a polygon),
$j = 60°$ (ext. angles of a polygon),
$k = 60°$ (angles at centre of a polygon)
5 $l = 38°$ (angles on a straight line)

6 $m = 29°$ (vert. opp. angles),
  $n = 61°$ (angles on a straight line),
  $p = 61°$ (angles on a straight line or at a point)

7 $q = 85°$ (supplementary angles),
  $r = 95°$ (corresponding angles),
  $s = 95°$ (vert. opp. angles),
  $t = 95°$ (corresponding angles)

8 $u = 64°$ (angles in a triangle),
  $v = 64°$ (vert. opp. angles),
  $w = 116°$ (angles on a straight line)

9 $x = 49°$ (vert. opp. angles),
  $y = 49°$ (corresponding angles)

10 $a = 63°$ (corresponding angles),
  $b = 63°$ (alternate angles),
  $c = 117°$ (supplementary angles)

11 $d = 46°$ (vert. opp. angles),
  $e = 44°$ (angles on a straight line),
  $f = 134°$ (supplementary angles),
  $g = 46°$ (corresponding angles)

12 $h = 45°$ (angles at a point)

63 RECOGNISING SYMMETRY

9

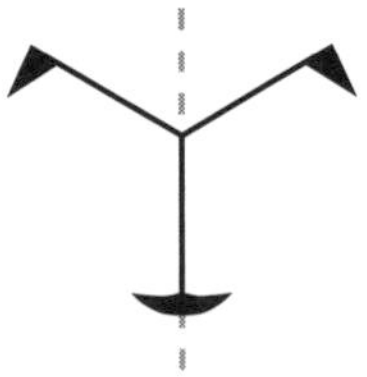

10
Order 2 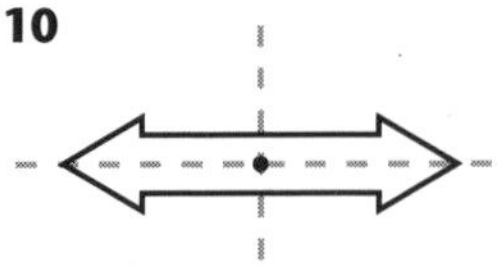

11 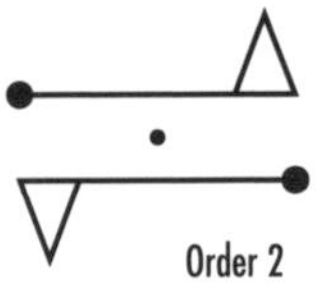
Order 2

12

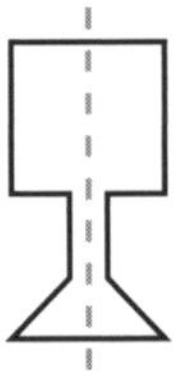

13
Order 4 

14 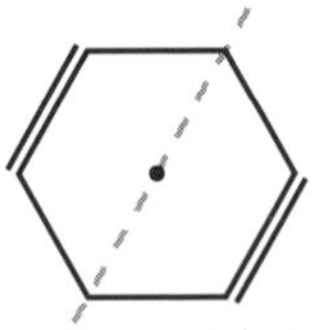
Order 2

15 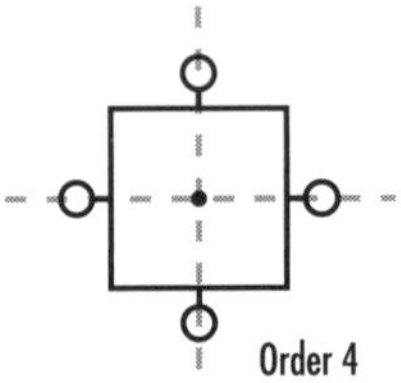
Order 4

16 
Order 3

Exercise 63A

1

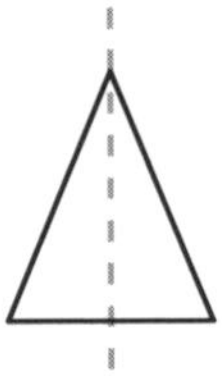

2
Order 4

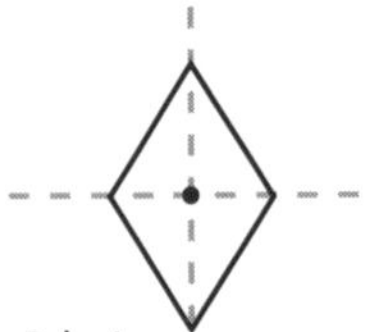

3

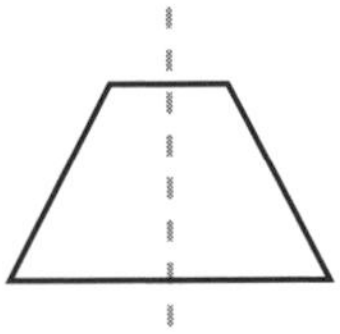

4
Order 6

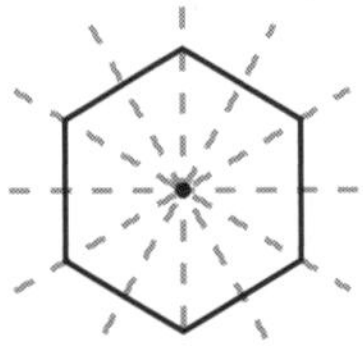

5
Order 2

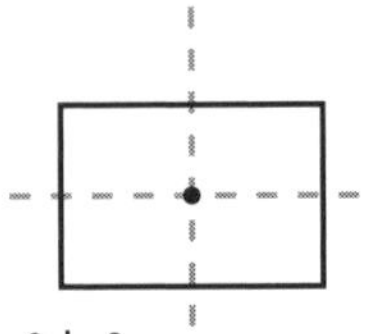

6
No symmetry

7

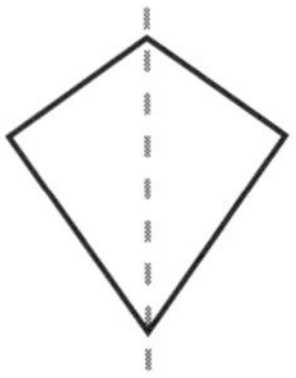

8
Order 5

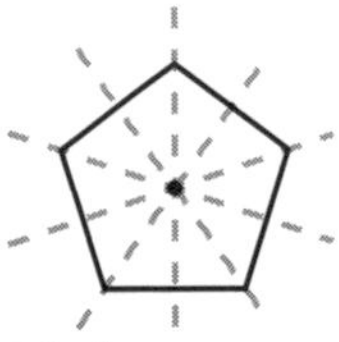

Exercise 63B

1 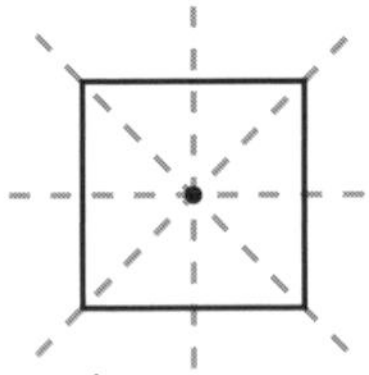
Order 4

2 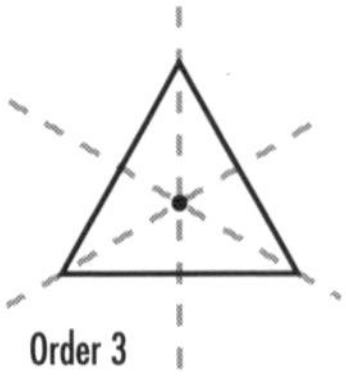
Order 3

3
No symmetry

4 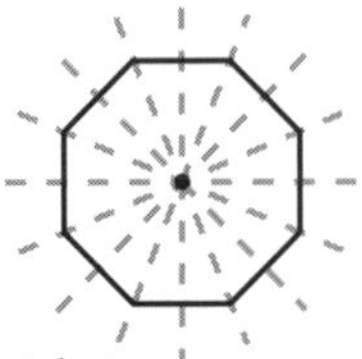
Order 8

5 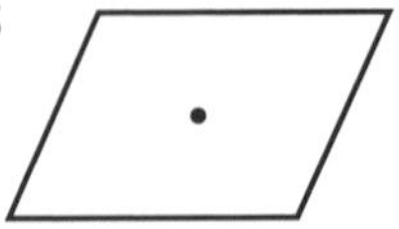
Order 2

6

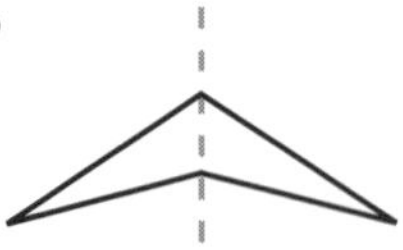

7

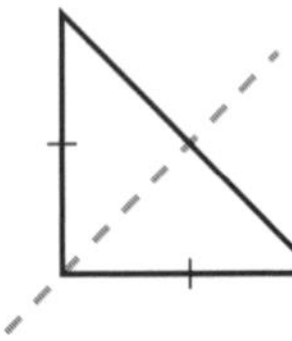

8
Order 7

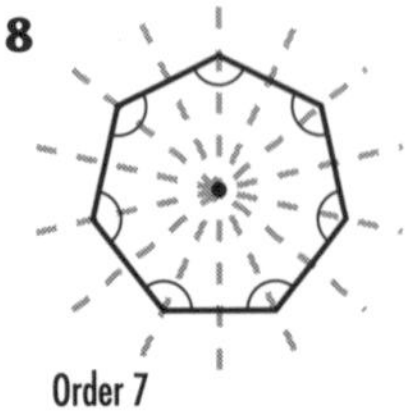

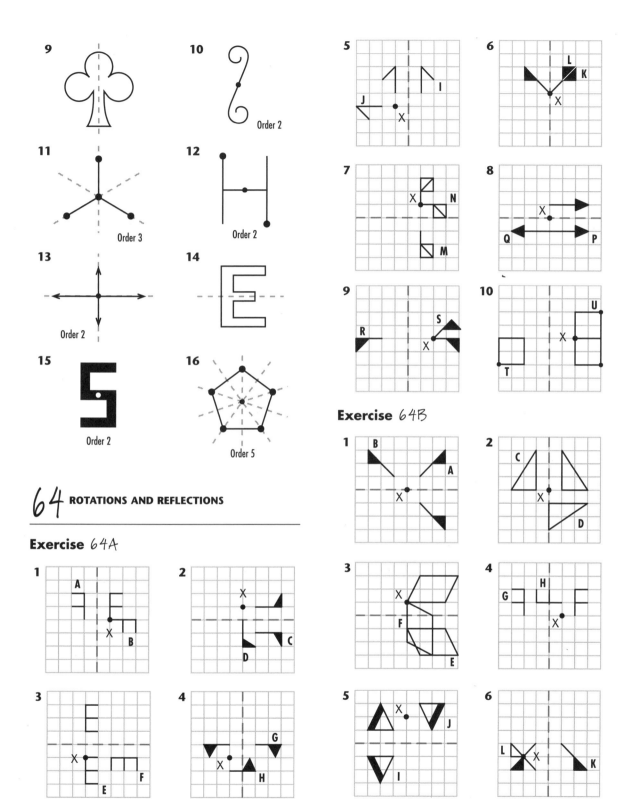

9
10 Order 2

11 Order 3
12 Order 2

13 Order 2
14

15 Order 2
16 Order 5

64 ROTATIONS AND REFLECTIONS

Exercise 64A

1 A, B, X
2 X, C, D
3 X, E, F
4 G, X, H

5 J, I, X
6 L, K, X
7 X, N, M
8 X, Q, P
9 R, S, X
10 U, X, T

Exercise 64B

1 B, A, X
2 C, X, D
3 X, F, E
4 G, H, X
5 X, J, I
6 L, X, K

7

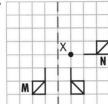

8

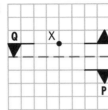

9

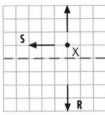

10

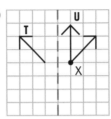

ℝEVISION

Exercise E

1 38°, 152

2 Check accuracy of angles.

3 $a = 69°$, $b = 111°$, $c = 90°$, $d = 142°$, $e = 108°$,
$f = 140°$, $g = 27°$, $h = 72°$, $i = 72°$, $j = 108°$,
$k = 70°$, $l = 70°$, $m = 110°$, $n = 227°$, $p = 37°$,
$q = 143°$

4 (a) Parallelogram   (b) Isosceles triangle
   (c) Trapezium   (d) Kite
   (e) Rhombus   (f) Pentagon

5 (a)   (b)   (c)

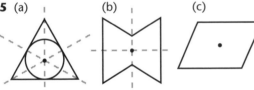

6

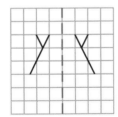

7

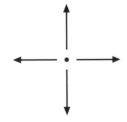

Exercise EE

1 (a)   (b)

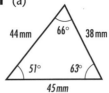 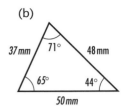

2 $a = 70°$, $b = 40°$, $c = 50°$, $d = 50°$, $e = 80°$,
$f = 30°$, $g = 30°$

3 (a) $p = 70°$, $q = 110°$, $r = 70°$, $s = 110°$
   (b) BCGF isosceles trapezium, ABED
     parallelogram, BIJ right-angled triangle,
     BEF isosceles triangle, DEIH trapezium

4 $a = 69°$ (angles of isos. triangle), $b = 69°$
(angles of isos. triangle), $c = 65°$ (straight line),
$d = 65°$ (supplementary angles), $e = 158°$
(angles at a point), $f = 60°$ (ext. angle of
hexagon), $g = 120°$ (int. angle of hexagon),
$h = 44°$ (vert. opp.), $i = 136°$ (straight line),
$j = 54°$ (alternate), $k = 54°$ (corresponding)

5 9

6 45°, 135°

7

no symmetry

8

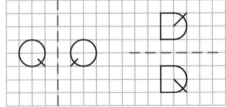

9

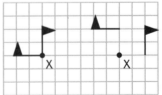

10

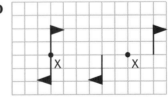

65 UNDERSTANDING SCALE

Exercise 65A

1 3 m	2 5.4 km
3 15 km	4 83 km
5 130 m	6 520 km
7 10 mm	8 7 cm
9 6 mm	10 6 cm

11 26 mm by 9 mm, 260 m by 90 m*
12 28 mm, 28 km*

13 28 mm, 7 km*	14 28 mm, 1.1 mile*
15 18 mm, 18 km*	16 12 mm, 3 km*
17 17 mm, 0.7 mile*	18 7 mm, 70 m*
19 40 mm, 40 km*	20 30 mm, 7.5 km*

Exercise 65B

1 5.8 km	2 75 m
3 41 km	4 7 km
5 110 m	6 46 km
7 1 mm	8 40 mm
9 15 mm	10 5.5 inches
11 44 mm, 44 km*	12 34 mm, 340 m*
13 20 mm, 0.8 mile*	14 12 mm, 23 km*
15 23 mm, 23 km*	16 21 mm, 210 m*
17 67 mm, 2.7 mile*	18 52 mm, 13 km*
19 14 mm, 14 km*	20 21 mm, 0.84 mile*

*Student measurement may differ from the stated value; allow follow through for their answer (provided that their measurement is approximately correct).

66 DRAWING TO SCALE

Student's diagrams should be drawn to the exact dimensions given.

Exercise 66A

1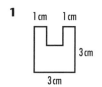

2

3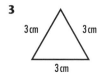

4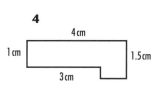

5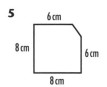

6

7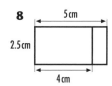

8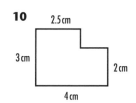

9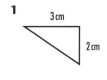

10

Exercise 66B

1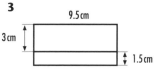

2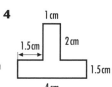

3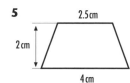

4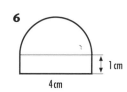

5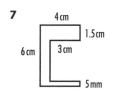

6

7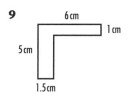

8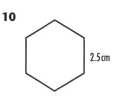

9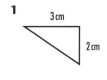

10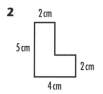

67 FINDING THE SCALE FACTOR AND CENTRE OF ENLARGEMENT

Exercise 67A

1
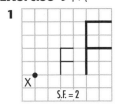
S.F. = 2

2
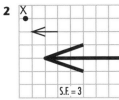
S.F. = 3

3
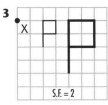
S.F. = 2

4
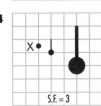
S.F. = 3

5
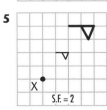
S.F. = 2

6
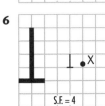
S.F. = 4

7
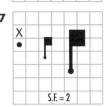
S.F. = 2

8
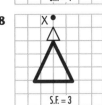
S.F. = 3

9
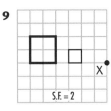
S.F. = 2

10
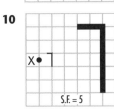
S.F. = 5

Exercise 67B

1
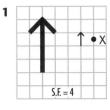
S.F. = 4

2
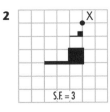
S.F. = 3

3
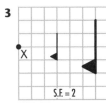
S.F. = 2

4
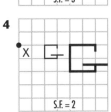
S.F. = 2

5
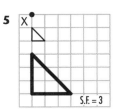
S.F. = 3

6
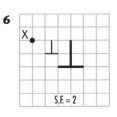
S.F. = 2

7
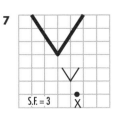
S.F. = 3

8
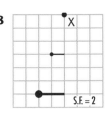
S.F. = 2

9
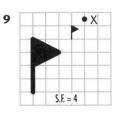
S.F. = 4

10
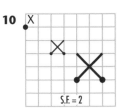
S.F. = 2

68 DRAWING ENLARGEMENTS

Exercise 68A

1
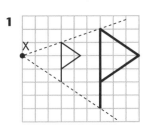

2
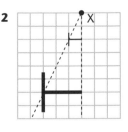

3
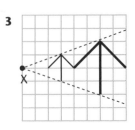

4
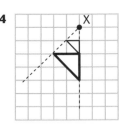

5
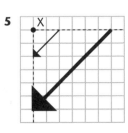

6
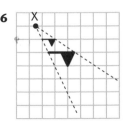

7 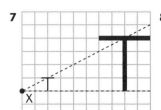 **8**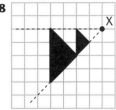

9 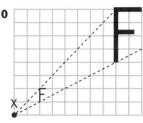 **10**

9 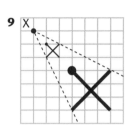 **10**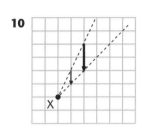

Exercise 68B

1 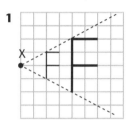 **2**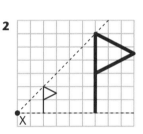

3 **4**

5 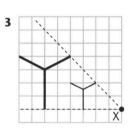 **6**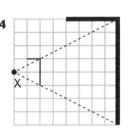

7 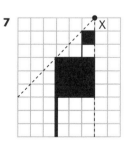 **8**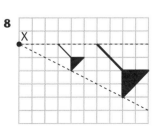

69 METRIC UNITS

Exercise 69A

1 4000 mm	**2** 3.5 kg	**3** 250 cl
4 55 cl	**5** 35 mm	**6** 7450 g
7 17 cm	**8** 4.5 g	**9** 750 ml
10 2300 kg	**11** 4750 m	**12** 35 kg
13 600 cm	**14** 0.75 l	**15** 1435 ml
16 17 500 g	**17** 375 mm	**18** 17.5 g
19 4665 kg	**20** 50 cl	**21** 11 250 g
22 7.5 m	**23** 450 ml	**24** 7 g
25 12.5 g	**26** 1.3 m	**27** 7750 m
28 500 ml	**29** 1250 kg	**30** 25 cm

Exercise 69B

1 2.5 kg	**2** 3400 cm	**3** 7 l
4 12 000 kg	**5** 34 cm	**6** 3200 l
7 13 600 g	**8** 1.75 m	**9** 150 cl
10 65 m	**11** 0.976 l	**12** 3000 g
13 45 g	**14** 3540 g	**15** 467.5 cm
16 1045 kg	**17** 4.5 l	**18** 3500 m
19 0.125 m	**20** 350 cl	**21** 2.735 kg
22 1350 ml	**23** 350 mm	**24** 2 mg
25 3.4 m	**26** 126.5 cm	**27** 3 000 000 g
28 45 cl	**29** 500 g	**30** 250 m

Exercise 69C

1 9	**2** 360 ml	**3** 25
4 750 kg	**5** 20	
6 435 cm or 4.35 m		**7** 40
8 43 mg	**9** 124 mm	**10** 14 l

Exercise 69D

1 120 g	**2** 14.350 km	**3** 20 ml
4 3	**5** 45 mm	**6** 750 mg
7 5	**8** 550 cm	**9** 2.1 t
10 10		

70 SENSIBLE ESTIMATES

Exercise 70A

1 J	**2** S	**3** K	**4** A	**5** F
6 D	**7** B	**8** P	**9** G	**10** H

11 T	12 E	13 L	14 R	15 O
16 N	17 C	18 Q	19 M	20 I

Exercise 70B

1 C	2 G	3 S	4 H	5 D
6 K	7 M	8 N	9 O	10 E
11 A	12 L	13 Q	14 T	15 J
16 R	17 B	18 F	19 I	20 P

71 IMPERIAL AND METRIC UNITS

Exercise 71A

1 20 m	2 2 gal	3 20 kg
4 2.5 ft	5 2 in	6 10 miles
7 21 pt	8 20 st	9 11 yd
10 10 kg	11 8 *l*	12 18 *l*
13 100 mm	14 90 cm	15 160 km
16 50 m	17 2200 lb	18 60 in
19 45 cm	20 65 kg	21 35 cm
22 80 m.p.h.	23 50 kg	24 450 g
25 75 cm	26 0.6 in	27 Heavier, no
28 4 gal	29 110 lb, 2 lb lighter	
30 4 *l*		

Exercise 71B

1 4 ft	2 44 lb	3 27 *l*
4 15 kg	5 96 km	6 39 kg
7 2.5 ft	8 22 yd	9 14 pt
10 40 miles	11 100 m	12 10 st
13 17.5 pt	14 66 yd	15 22 lb
16 50 miles	17 10 in	18 800 m
19 12 *l*	20 25 kg	21 64 km
22 65 kg	23 8 in	
24 66 ft or 67 ft depending on method		
25 4 st	26 36 *l*	27 200 cl
28 1 pint	29 45 miles	30 1 ton

72 NETS

Exercise 72A

1 15 mm · 15 mm · 15 mm · 15 mm · 15 mm · 15 mm · 30 mm

2 1 cm · 1 cm · 4 cm · 1 cm · 4 cm · 3 cm

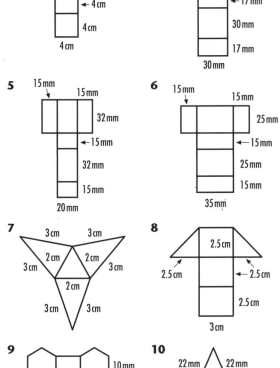

3 4 cm · 4 cm · 4 cm · 4 cm · 4 cm · 4 cm

4 17 mm · 17 mm · 30 mm · 17 mm · 30 mm · 17 mm · 30 mm

5 15 mm · 15 mm · 32 mm · 15 mm · 32 mm · 15 mm · 20 mm

6 15 mm · 15 mm · 25 mm · 15 mm · 25 mm · 15 mm · 35 mm

7 3 cm · 3 cm · 2 cm · 2 cm · 3 cm · 3 cm · 2 cm · 3 cm · 3 cm

8 2.5 cm · 2.5 cm · 2.5 cm · 2.5 cm · 3 cm

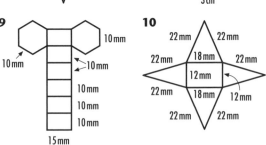

9 10 mm · 10 mm · 10 mm · 10 mm · 10 mm · 10 mm · 15 mm

10 22 mm · 22 mm · 22 mm · 18 mm · 22 mm · 12 mm · 22 mm · 18 mm · 12 mm · 22 mm · 22 mm

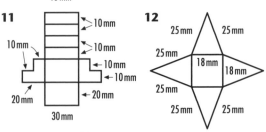

11 10 mm · 10 mm · 10 mm · 10 mm · 10 mm · 20 mm · 20 mm · 30 mm

12 25 mm · 25 mm · 25 mm · 18 mm · 18 mm · 25 mm · 25 mm · 25 mm

Exercise 72B

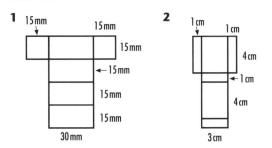

1 12 mm · 12 mm · 28 mm · 12 mm · 28 mm · 12 mm · 35 mm

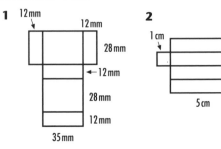

2 1 cm · 1 cm · 1 cm · 1 cm · 5 cm

3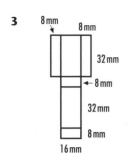

4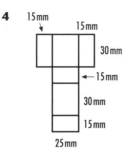

5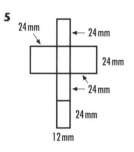

6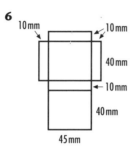

7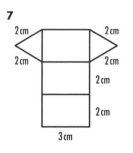

8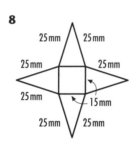

9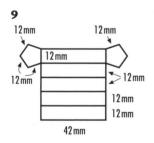

10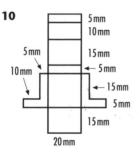

11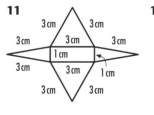

12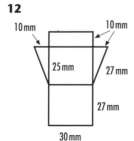

73 AREAS OF SQUARES, RECTANGLES AND PARALLELOGRAMS

Exercise 73A

1 12 cm^2	**2** 36 cm^2	**3** 12.5 cm^2
4 28 cm^2	**5** 1200 mm^2	**6** 6.25 m^2
7 1.08 m^2	**8** 1000 mm^2	**9** 144 cm^2
10 60 cm^2	**11** 0.64 m^2	**12** 120 mm^2
13 91 cm^2	**14** 2100 mm^2	**15** 441 mm^2
16 18.29 cm^2	**17** 4.76 cm^2	**18** 361 mm^2
19 38 m^2	**20** 33 cm^2	

Exercise 73B

1 24 cm^2	**2** 5.76 m^2	**3** 230 mm^2
4 49 m^2	**5** 30 cm^2	**6** 196 cm^2
7 272 mm^2	**8** 400 cm^2	**9** 6000 mm^2
10 90 cm^2	**11** 0.64 m^2	**12** 242 cm^2
13 17.64 cm^2	**14** 289 mm^2	**15** 102 cm^2
16 17.68 cm^2	**17** 390 mm^2	**18** 30 cm^2
19 18 cm^2	**20** $259\,200 \text{ cm}^2$ or 25.92 m^2	

74 AREA OF A TRIANGLE

Exercise 74A

1 6 cm^2	**2** 15 cm^2	**3** 14 cm^2
4 120 mm^2	**5** 40 cm^2	**6** 48 cm^2
7 119 mm^2	**8** 1.4 m^2	**9** 250 mm^2
10 210 cm^2	**11** 24.5 cm^2	**12** 13.5 m^2
13 9.3 m^2	**14** 2.56 cm^2	**15** 0.24 m^2
16 3700 mm^2	**17** 9 cm^2	**18** 30 cm^2
19 12.18 m^2	**20** 3 cm^2 or 300 mm^2	

Exercise 74B

1 9 cm^2	**2** 18 cm^2	**3** 10 cm^2
4 36 cm^2	**5** 240 mm^2	**6** 0.16 m^2
7 1600 mm^2	**8** 66 cm^2	**9** 12 cm^2
10 360 mm^2	**11** 0.84 m^2	**12** 1176 mm^2
13 880 cm^2	**14** 160 cm^2	**15** 2.88 m^2
16 2.16 m^2	**17** 12 cm^2	**18** 63 m^2
19 48 cm^2	**20** 30 cm^2	

75 AREA OF A TRAPEZIUM

Exercise 75A

1 24 cm^2	**2** 24 cm^2	**3** 20 cm^2
4 40 cm^2	**5** 189 mm^2	**6** 38 cm^2
7 170 cm^2	**8** 121 cm^2	**9** 70 cm^2
10 15 cm^2	**11** 900 mm^2	**12** 22.4 cm^2

13 $0.22\,\text{m}^2$ **14** $594\,\text{mm}^2$ **15** $1.68\,\text{m}^2$
16 $24\,\text{cm}^2$ **17** $684\,\text{cm}^2$ **18** $1020\,\text{mm}^2$
19 $10.35\,\text{m}^2$ **20** $19.8\,\text{cm}^2$ or $1980\,\text{mm}^2$

Exercise 75B

1 $60\,\text{cm}^2$ **2** $9\,\text{cm}^2$ **3** $48\,\text{cm}^2$
4 $108\,\text{cm}^2$ **5** $20\,\text{cm}^2$ **6** $160\,\text{mm}^2$
7 $70\,\text{cm}^2$ **8** $66\,\text{cm}^2$ **9** $210\,\text{mm}^2$
10 $49\,\text{cm}^2$ **11** $0.44\,\text{m}^2$ **12** $900\,\text{mm}^2$
13 $310\,\text{cm}^2$ **14** $13.5\,\text{cm}^2$ **15** $69\,\text{cm}^2$
16 $14.4\,\text{m}^2$ **17** $644\,\text{mm}^2$
18 $1850\,\text{mm}^2$ or $18.5\,\text{cm}^2$
19 $150\,\text{cm}^2$ **20** $4550\,\text{mm}^2$ or $45.5\,\text{cm}^2$

76 VOLUMES OF CUBES AND CUBOIDS

Exercise 76A

1 $125\,\text{cm}^3$ **2** $105\,\text{cm}^3$ **3** $2400\,\text{mm}^3$
4 $27\,\text{cm}^3$ **5** $168\,\text{cm}^3$ **6** $384\,\text{mm}^3$
7 $3.375\,\text{cm}^3$ **8** $480\,\text{cm}^3$ **9** $27\,000\,\text{mm}^3$
10 $0.105\,\text{m}^3$ **11** $729\,\text{cm}^3$ **12** $8.8\,\text{cm}^3$
13 $45\,360\,\text{mm}^3$ **14** $0.729\,\text{m}^3$ **15** $17.5\,\text{cm}^3$
16 $9000\,\text{mm}^3$ or $9\,\text{cm}^3$ **17** $216\,\text{cm}^3$
18 $10\,500\,\text{mm}^3$ **19** $90\,\text{cm}^3$ **20** $23.94\,\text{cm}^3$

Exercise 76B

1 $96\,\text{cm}^3$ **2** $216\,\text{cm}^3$ **3** $960\,\text{cm}^3$
4 $224\,\text{cm}^3$ **5** $64\,\text{cm}^3$ **6** $1040\,\text{cm}^3$
7 $672\,\text{cm}^3$ **8** $0.216\,\text{m}^3$ **9** $86\,016\,\text{mm}^3$
10 $9261\,\text{mm}^3$ **11** $0.21\,\text{m}^3$ **12** $7.875\,\text{cm}^3$
13 $1331\,\text{cm}^3$ **14** $1.32\,\text{m}^3$ **15** $30\,\text{cm}^3$
16 $17\,280\,\text{mm}^3$ **17** $16.896\,\text{cm}^3$ **18** $125\,\text{cm}^3$
19 $192\,\text{cm}^3$ or $192\,000\,\text{mm}^3$
20 $61.2\,\text{cm}^3$ or $61\,200\,\text{mm}^3$

77 CIRCUMFERENCE OF A CIRCLE

Exercise 77A
Answers are to 3 s.f.

1 $37.7\,\text{cm}$ **2** $25.1\,\text{cm}$ **3** $37.7\,\text{m}$
4 $31.4\,\text{cm}$ **5** $50.2\,\text{mm}$ **6** $15.7\,\text{cm}$
7 $75.4\,\text{mm}$ **8** $7.85\,\text{m}$ **9** $10.0\,\text{cm}$
10 $94.2\,\text{cm}$ **11** $37.7\,\text{cm}$ **12** $7.54\,\text{m}$
13 $11.3\,\text{cm}$ **14** $53.4\,\text{cm}$ **15** $56.6\,\text{cm}$
16 $44.0\,\text{cm}$ **17** $22.0\,\text{cm}$ **18** $66.0\,\text{cm}$
19 $22.0\,\text{m}$ **20** $66.0\,\text{mm}$ **21** $20.4\,\text{cm}$
22 $50.2\,\text{mm}$ **23** $107\,\text{cm}$ **24** $20.1\,\text{cm}$
25 $57.8\,\text{cm}$ **26** $62.8\,\text{cm}$ **27** $87.9\,\text{cm}$
28 $53.4\,\text{cm}$ **29** $4.40\,\text{m}$ **30** $30.2\,\text{m}$

Exercise 77B
Answers are to 3 s.f.

1 $62.8\,\text{cm}$ **2** $25.1\,\text{mm}$ **3** $56.5\,\text{cm}$
4 $100\,\text{mm}$ **5** $47.1\,\text{cm}$ **6** $32.0\,\text{cm}$
7 $18.8\,\text{cm}$ **8** $28.3\,\text{m}$ **9** $34.5\,\text{cm}$
10 $47.1\,\text{cm}$ **11** $7.85\,\text{m}$ **12** $17.0\,\text{cm}$
13 $408\,\text{mm}$ **14** $72.3\,\text{cm}$ **15** $5.66\,\text{m}$
16 $176\,\text{cm}$ **17** $5.66\,\text{m}$ **18** $23.9\,\text{m}$
19 $110\,\text{mm}$ **20** $132\,\text{mm}$ **21** $157\,\text{cm}$
22 $28.9\,\text{m}$ **23** $251\,\text{mm}$ **24** $308\,\text{mm}$
25 $352\,\text{mm}$ **26** $20.1\,\text{m}$ **27** $2.36\,\text{m}$
28 $377\,\text{mm}$ **29** $8.79\,\text{m}$ **30** $9.11\,\text{m}$

78 AREA OF A CIRCLE

Exercise 78A
Answers are to 3 s.f.

1 $113\,\text{cm}^2$ **2** $50.2\,\text{cm}^2$ **3** $113\,\text{m}^2$
4 $78.5\,\text{cm}^2$ **5** $201\,\text{mm}^2$ **6** $19.6\,\text{cm}^2$
7 $452\,\text{mm}^2$ **8** $4.91\,\text{m}^2$ **9** $8.04\,\text{cm}^2$
10 $707\,\text{cm}^2$ **11** $113\,\text{cm}^2$ **12** $4.52\,\text{m}^2$
13 $10.2\,\text{cm}^2$ **14** $227\,\text{cm}^2$ **15** $254\,\text{cm}^2$
16 $154\,\text{cm}^2$ **17** $38.5\,\text{cm}^2$ **18** $346\,\text{cm}^2$
19 $38.5\,\text{m}^2$ **20** $346\,\text{mm}^2$ **21** $33.2\,\text{cm}^2$
22 $201\,\text{mm}^2$ **23** $907\,\text{cm}^2$ **24** $32.2\,\text{cm}^2$
25 $266\,\text{cm}^2$ **26** $314\,\text{cm}^2$ **27** $615\,\text{cm}^2$
28 $227\,\text{cm}^2$ **29** $1.54\,\text{m}^2$ **30** $72.4\,\text{m}^2$

Exercise 78B
Answers are to 3 s.f.

1 $314\,\text{cm}^2$ **2** $50.2\,\text{mm}^2$ **3** $254\,\text{cm}^2$
4 $804\,\text{mm}^2$ **5** $177\,\text{cm}^2$ **6** $81.7\,\text{cm}^2$
7 $28.3\,\text{cm}^2$ **8** $63.6\,\text{m}^2$ **9** $95.0\,\text{cm}^2$
10 $177\,\text{cm}^2$ **11** $4.91\,\text{m}^2$ **12** $22.9\,\text{cm}^2$
13 $13\,300\,\text{mm}^2$ **14** $416\,\text{cm}^2$ **15** $2.55\,\text{m}^2$
16 $2460\,\text{cm}^2$ **17** $2.55\,\text{m}^2$ **18** $45.4\,\text{m}^2$
19 $962\,\text{mm}^2$ **20** $1390\,\text{mm}^2$ **21** $1960\,\text{cm}^2$
22 $66.5\,\text{m}^2$ **23** $5020\,\text{mm}^2$ **24** $7540\,\text{mm}^2$
25 $9850\,\text{mm}^2$ **26** $32.3\,\text{m}^2$ **27** $0.442\,\text{m}^2$
28 $11\,300\,\text{mm}^2$ **29** $6.15\,\text{m}^2$ **30** $6.61\,\text{m}^2$

R EVISION

Exercise F

1 $7\,\text{km}$
2 $2\,\text{cm}$

3 _____ $2.7\,\text{cm}$

4 ——————— 2.3 cm

5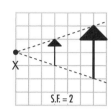

6 (a) 1200 mm   (b) 154 m   (c) 12.5 kg
     (d) 975 kg   (e) 3.4 *l*   (f) 75 000 ml

7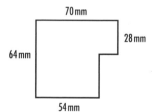

8 (a) 289 mm²   (b) 45 cm²   (c) 1.04 m²
     (d) 200 cm²   (e) 24 m²

9 C

10 91.125 cm³

11 154.56 cm³

12 32.05 cm

13 78.5 m²

Exercise *FF*

1 3 cm, 1.2 mile, or follow through reasonable measurement.

2 7 cm, 70 km, or follow through reasonable measurement.

3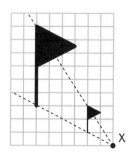

4

5 Yes! by 6 or 7 kg (6.25)

6 162 litres

7 0.0025 t

8 4.5 m

9 Sugar by 4 lb or 2 kg

10 100 000 cm³, 100 *l*

11 4 cm

12 No, it is short by approximately 5.7 cm

13 (a) 78.55 m²   (b) 3930 g

14 (a) 12 cm²   (b) 52 cm²   (c) 18 cm²
     (d) 2250 mm²   (e) 13.5 m²

Handling data

79 MEAN AND RANGE

Exercise 79A

1 (a) 6	(b) 8	**2** (a) 4.6	(b) 7
3 (a) 11	(b) 8	**4** (a) 43	(b) 42
5 (a) 4	(b) 4	**6** (a) 6.5	(b) 11
7 (a) 30	(b) 14	**8** (a) 5	(b) 8
9 (a) 6	(b) 10	**10** (a) 14.5	(b) 7
11 (a) 3	(b) 7	**12** (a) 8	(b) 9
13 (a) 3.1	(b) 9	**14** (a) 37	(b) 51
15 (a) 4.5	(b) 8	**16** (a) 33.5	(b) 53
17 (a) 0.6	(b) 0.7	**18** (a) 1.8	(b) 2.8
19 (a) 103	(b) 4	**20** (a) 43.7	(b) 14

Exercise 79B

1 (a) 5	(b) 5	**2** (a) 3	(b) 4
3 (a) 7	(b) 10	**4** (a) 20	(b) 7
5 (a) 3	(b) 6	**6** (a) 10	(b) 11
7 (a) 6.5	(b) 8	**8** (a) 57	(b) 45
9 (a) 15	(b) 9	**10** (a) 37	(b) 74
11 (a) 4.5	(b) 7	**12** (a) 8	(b) 7
13 (a) 60	(b) 65	**14** (a) 11.25	(b) 9
15 (a) 44	(b) 12	**16** (a) 79.5	(b) 89
17 (a) 4.4	(b) 7	**18** (a) 15.25	(b) 22
19 (a) 1.2	(b) 0.8	**20** (a) 83.75	(b) 211

80 USING THE MEAN AND RANGE

Exercise 80A

1 119	**2** 16	**3** £65
4 24	**5** 27 mm	**6** 17°C
7 9	**8** 143	**9** 144 cm
10 65	**11** 6, 8	**12** 6
13 41		

14 Eastend: mean 14.50, range 14
Northpoint: mean 15.625, range 8
Northpoint has the highest mean and is also more reliable.

15 8A has the higher total. 8B is more likely to have the extremes.

Exercise 80B

1 9	**2** 273	**3** 31.5 km
4 12 hours	**5** 4	**6** 13.5
7 29	**8** 17 and 20	**9** 22°C
10 40	**11** 58 mm	**12** 6

13 Test 1: mean 45.67, range 68
Test 2: mean 77, range 22

14 Bus because, although they are less frequent, they are more reliable.

15 Means: coffee 6.8; tea 5.6
Ranges: coffee 5; tea 2
Coffee is more popular but tea has more reliable numbers.

81 CONTINUOUS DATA: CREATING FREQUENCY TABLES AND FREQUENCY DIAGRAMS

Exercise 81A

1

Weight (kg)	Frequency
$50 \leq w < 55$	4
$55 \leq w < 60$	7
$60 \leq w < 65$	9
$65 \leq w < 70$	5
Total	25

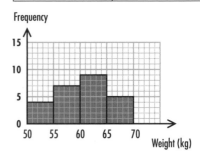

2

Length (cm)	Frequency
$7 \leq L < 8$	2
$8 \leq L < 9$	4
$9 \leq L < 10$	7
$10 \leq L < 11$	6
$11 \leq L < 12$	5
$12 \leq L < 13$	6
Total	30

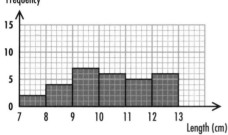

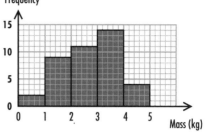

3

Speed (m.p.h.)	Frequency
$0 \leq S < 10$	3
$10 \leq S < 20$	4
$20 \leq S < 30$	6
$30 \leq S < 40$	12
$40 \leq S < 50$	9
$50 \leq S < 60$	6
Total	40

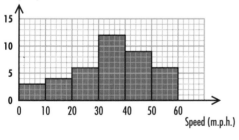

5

Capacity (ml)	Frequency
$400 \leq C < 450$	3
$450 \leq C < 500$	4
$500 \leq C < 550$	9
$550 \leq C < 600$	5
$600 \leq C < 650$	6
$650 \leq C < 700$	3
Total	30

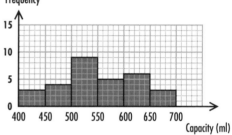

6

Miles	Frequency
$10 \leq M < 20$	1
$20 \leq M < 30$	2
$30 \leq M < 40$	7
$40 \leq M < 50$	12
$50 \leq M < 60$	6
$60 \leq M < 70$	2
Total	30

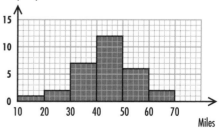

4

Mass (kg)	Frequency
$0 \leq M < 1$	2
$1 \leq M < 2$	9
$2 \leq M < 3$	11
$3 \leq M < 4$	14
$4 \leq M < 5$	4
Total	40

7

Time (s)	Frequency
$15 \leq T < 16$	2
$16 \leq T < 17$	3
$17 \leq T < 18$	8
$18 \leq T < 19$	11
$19 \leq T < 20$	12
$20 \leq T < 21$	4
Total	40

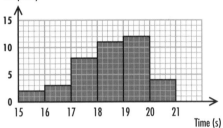

8

Weight (kg)	Frequency
$30 \leq w < 40$	5
$40 \leq w < 50$	13
$50 \leq w < 60$	12
$60 \leq w < 70$	6
$70 \leq w < 80$	3
$80 \leq w < 90$	1
Total	40

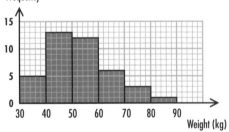

9

Distance (m)	Frequency
$0 \leq d < 25$	3
$25 \leq d < 50$	6
$50 \leq d < 75$	10
$75 \leq d < 100$	7
$100 \leq d < 125$	9
$125 \leq d < 150$	6
$150 \leq d < 175$	4
Total	45

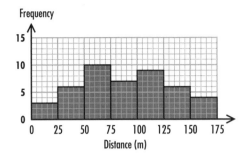

10

Mass (kg)	Frequency
$40 \leq M < 50$	4
$50 \leq M < 60$	7
$60 \leq M < 70$	11
$70 \leq M < 80$	16
$80 \leq M < 90$	9
$90 \leq M < 100$	3
Total	50

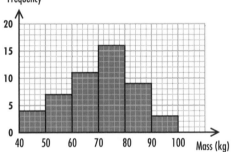

Exercise 81B

1

Time (s)	Frequency
$0 \leq T < 5$	2
$5 \leq T < 10$	8
$10 \leq T < 15$	4
$15 \leq T < 20$	6
$20 \leq T < 25$	7
$25 \leq T < 30$	5
$30 \leq T < 35$	3
Total	35

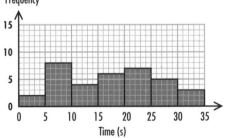

2

Mass (t)	Frequency
$0 \le M < 2$	13
$2 \le M < 4$	8
$4 \le M < 6$	4
$6 \le M < 8$	3
$8 \le M < 10$	2
Total	30

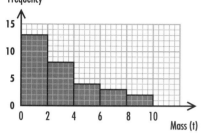

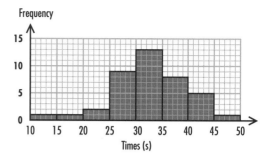

3

Age (years)	Frequency
$15 \le y < 20$	10
$20 \le y < 25$	8
$25 \le y < 30$	6
$30 \le y < 35$	6
$35 \le y < 40$	5
$40 \le y < 45$	5
Total	40

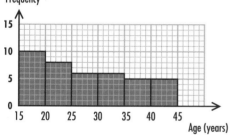

5

Distance (m)	Frequency
$30 \le d < 40$	3
$40 \le d < 50$	5
$50 \le d < 60$	7
$60 \le d < 70$	9
$70 \le d < 80$	9
$80 \le d < 90$	5
$90 \le d < 100$	2
Total	40

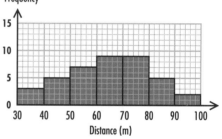

4

Times (s)	Frequency
$10 \le T < 15$	1
$15 \le T < 20$	1
$20 \le T < 25$	2
$25 \le T < 30$	9
$30 \le T < 35$	13
$35 \le T < 40$	8
$40 \le T < 45$	5
$45 \le T < 50$	1
Total	40

6

Mass (kg)	Frequency
$9 \le M < 10$	1
$10 \le M < 11$	4
$11 \le M < 12$	6
$12 \le M < 13$	8
$13 \le M < 14$	5
$14 \le M < 15$	8
$15 \le M < 16$	3
Total	35

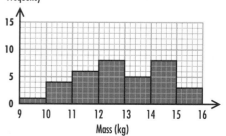

7

Height (cm)	Frequency
$140 \le h < 150$	4
$150 \le h < 160$	7
$160 \le h < 170$	7
$170 \le h < 180$	9
$180 \le h < 190$	4
$190 \le h < 200$	4
Total	35

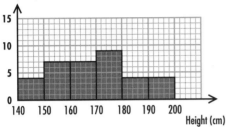

8

Area (m²)	Frequency
$0 \le A < 100$	4
$100 \le A < 200$	8
$200 \le A < 300$	3
$300 \le A < 400$	10
$400 \le A < 500$	7
$500 \le A < 600$	5
$600 \le A < 700$	3
Total	40

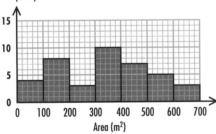

9

Yield (t)	Frequency
$0 \le y < 2$	5
$2 \le y < 4$	9
$4 \le y < 6$	18
$6 \le y < 8$	10
$8 \le y < 10$	5
$10 \le y < 12$	3
Total	50

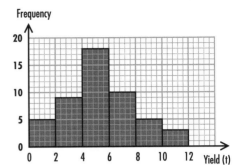

10

Wingspan (cm)	Frequency
$10 \le W < 12$	4
$12 \le W < 14$	9
$14 \le W < 16$	14
$16 \le W < 18$	10
$18 \le W < 20$	6
$20 \le W < 22$	2
Total	45

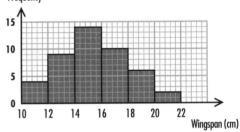

82 CONTINUOUS DATA: INTERPRETING FREQUENCY DIAGRAMS

Exercise 82A

1 (a) 35   (b) 6   (c) 8   (d) $\frac{1}{7}$

2 (a) 150–199   (b) 70   (c) 3   (d) 24.3%

3 (a) 21   (b) 9   (c) 39   (d) 51.7%

4 (a) 16   (b) 46   (c) 76   (d) $\frac{20}{76} = \frac{5}{19}$

5 (a) 900   (b) 110   (c) 420   (d) 53.3%

6 (a) 0   (b) 2   (c) 65   (d) 72.3%

Exercise 82B

1 (a) 30   (b) 5   (c) 1   (d) 40%

2 (a) 120   (b) 29   (c) 7   (d) $\frac{9}{120} = \frac{3}{40}$

3 (a) 210   (b) 31   (c) 72   (d) 20–24.9°C

4 (a) 540   (b) 2 kg   (c) 70   (d) 33.3%

5 (a) 16   (b) 14   (c) 7   (d) $\frac{2}{50} = \frac{1}{25}$

6 (a) 60   (b) 29   (c) 3   (d) 20%

83 PIE CHARTS: CALCULATION OF ANGLES AND CONSTRUCTION

Exercise 83A

1 96°	**2** 126°	**3** 324°	**4** 240°
5 162°	**6** 171°	**7** 150°	**8** 300°
9 100°	**10** 165°	**11** 300°	**12** 75°
13 82.8°	**14** 180°	**15** 321.6°	**16** 52.5°
17 162°	**18** 7.2°	**19** 40°	**20** 72°

Exercise 83B

1 72°	**2** 84°	**3** 168°	**4** 81°
5 150°	**6** 100°	**7** 90°	**8** 168°
9 51°	**10** 336°	**11** 186°	**12** 144°
13 84°	**14** 43.0°	**15** 37.2°	**16** 12°
17 126.7°	**18** 22.8°	**19** 86.4°	**20** 92.2°

Exercise 83C

1 Energy type

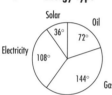

2 Car colours

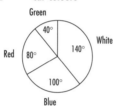

3 Grades

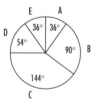

4 Holiday destinations

5 Weight of pupils (kg)

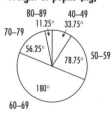

6 TV sports

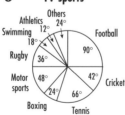

7 Use of home PCs

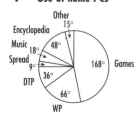

8 Score on a dice

9 UK holiday travel

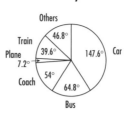

10 Imports

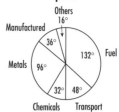

Exercise 83D

1 Homework time

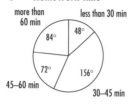

2 Crisp survey

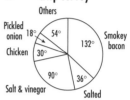

3 Favourite subjects

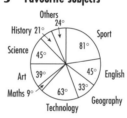

4 Favourite paper

5 Postage

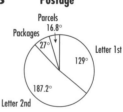

6 Pets

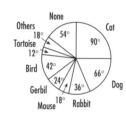

7 Ice cream

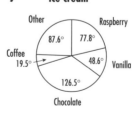

8 Ages on a day trip

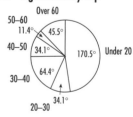

9 Expenditure

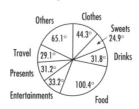

10 Supermarket survey

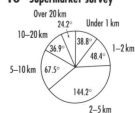

Exercise 84A

1 (a) 45   (b) 6   (c) 150–159 cm
(d) 132°, 33

2 (a) Rover   (b) Others   (c) 270
(d) 160°, 120

3 (a) Bus   (b) Walk
(c) $\frac{45}{300} \times 360° = 54°$ (d) 120°, 100

4 (a) Dog   (b) Cat   (c) 6°, 60
(d) 18°, 3

5 (a) Solar   (b) 7.5°   (c) $\frac{150}{360} \times 48 = 20$
(d) 75°, 10

6 (a) Lolly   (b) $\frac{1}{4}$ (c) 5°, 72
(d) 80°, 16

7 (a) Other   (b) Communication
(c) $\frac{60}{360} \times 300 = 50$ (d) 72°, 60

8 (a) 20–24   (b) Under 10   (c) 4°
(d) $\frac{360}{4} = 90$

Exercise 84B

1 (a) Black   (b) Green   (c) 40°
(d) 120°, 9

2 (a) Cereal and Toast   (b) Fried breakfast
(c) $\frac{48}{360} \times 60 = 8$ (d) 60°, 10

3 (a) Letter 1st   (b) Less than 500 g
(c) 8°   (d) 48°, 18

4 (a) 1–2 km   (b) 10–20 km and 2–5 km
(c) $\frac{60}{360} \times 150 = 25$ (d) 48°, 20

5 (a) Very poor   (b) Quite good and Good
(c) $\frac{30}{360} \times 60 = 5$ (d) 48°, 8

6 (a) Heart   (b) Heart and Diamond
(c) Spade   (d) 12°, 2

7 (a) 75   (b) Tennis   (c) $\frac{24}{360} \times 150 = 10$
(d) 36°, 15

8 (a) Washing up   (b) Ironing
(c) 3.6°   (d) $\frac{360}{3.6} = 100$

Exercise 85A

1

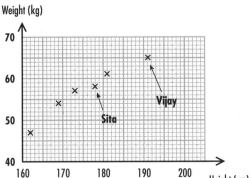

2

3

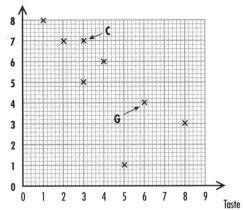

4

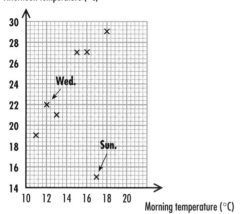

Afternoon temperature (°C) / Morning temperature (°C)

5

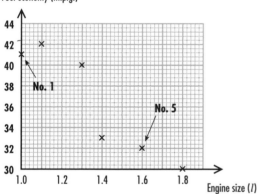

Fuel economy (m.p.g.) / Engine size (l)

6

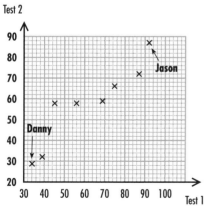

Test 2 / Test 1

7

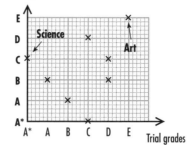

GCSE grades / Trial grades

8

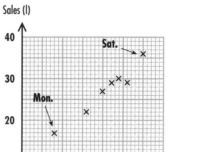

Sales (l) / Temperature (°C)

Exercise 85B

1

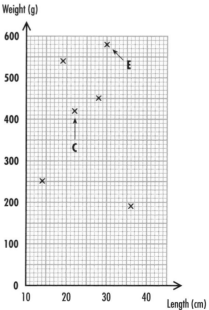

Weight (g) / Length (cm)

2

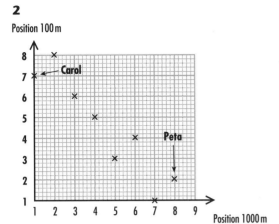

3

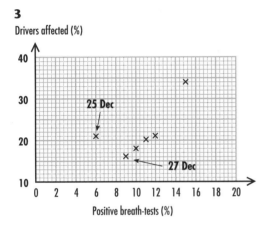

4

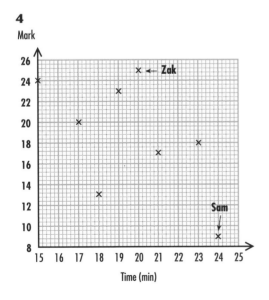

5

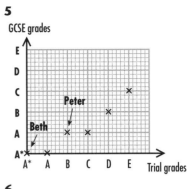

6

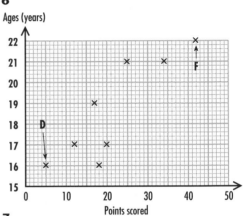

7

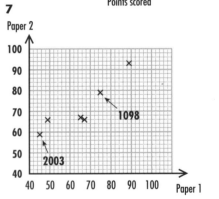

8

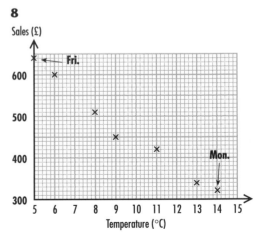

86 CORRELATION

Exercise 86A

1 Negative	**2** Perfect positive
3 No correlation	**4** Positive
5 Perfect negative	**6** No correlation
7 Positive	**8** Positive
9 Perfect negative	**10** Perfect positive
11 No correlation	**12** Negative

Exercise 86B

1 Positive	**2** Negative (slight)
3 No correlation	**4** Perfect positive
5 Positive	**6** Perfect negative
7 Negative	**8** No correlation
9 Perfect positive	**10** Positive
11 No correlation	**12** Positive (slight)

Exercise 86C

1 Perfect positive	**2** Good negative
3 Good positive	**4** Good positive
5 Good negative	**6** Good positive
7 Moderate positive	**8** Good positive

Exercise 86D

1 Moderate positive	**2** Good negative
3 Good positive	**4** Some negative
5 Good positive	**6** Good positive
7 Good positive	**8** Perfect negative

R EVISION

Exercise G

1 (a) (i) £17 (ii) £14
(b) (i) 108.4 (ii) (b) 54

2

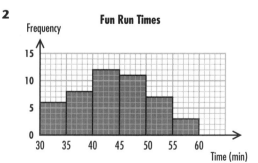
Fun Run Times

3 (a) 90° (b) 36° (c) 25°

---

4 Carpet tiles

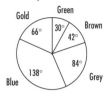

5 (a) (Perfect) positive (b) None
(c) Negative (d) (Some) positive

Exercise GG

1 16 years

2 138

3 9

4 84 kg

5 (a) 200 (b) 54 (c) 62 (d) 69%

6 (a) Bus (b) 3° (c) Walk and Other
(d) 24°, 8

7 (a) and (b)

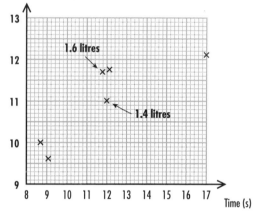
Fuel economy (km/l)

(c) Good positive correlation – fuel economy
is better for slower models.

87 ESTIMATING PROBABILITIES

Exercise 87A

1 0.1–0.2	**2** 0.4–0.6
3 0.05–0.3	**4** 1
5 0.2–0.4	**6** 0
7 0.6–0.95	**8** Low value around 0.1
9 Low value 0.05–0.2	**10** 0.4–0.6
11 Low value such as 0.1	**12** 0.4–0.6
13 0.8–0.9	**14** Low but not 0
15 0.7–0.8	**16** 0.8–0.95
17 0	**18** 0.5–0.9

19 Less than 0.5, probably 0.1–0.3

20 Discretionary!

Exercise 87B

1 0.6–0.95	**2** 0.2–0.3
3 1	**4** 0.1–0.45
5 Very low but not 0	**6** 0.6–0.8
7 0.05–0.2	**8** Very low but not 0
9 0 or close	**10** Low but not 0
11 Approximately 0.5	**12** High but not 1
13 High value around 0.9	
14 0.3–0.45	
15 0.5–0.95	**16** 0.4–0.6
17 0.7–0.95	**18** 0.15–0.25
19 0.5 or very close	**20** High but not 1

88 CALCULATING SIMPLE PROBABILITIES

Exercise 88A

1 $\frac{1}{5}$	**2** $\frac{4}{9}$	**3** 0.5	**4** $\frac{1}{6}$
5 0.375	**6** $\frac{1}{7}$	**7** 0.05	**8** $\frac{1}{4}$
9 $\frac{2}{7}$	**10** 0.5	**11** 0	**12** 0.25
13 $\frac{2}{7}$	**14** 0.5	**15** $\frac{1}{4}$	**16** 0.714
17 $\frac{1}{13}$	**18** 0.04	**19** $\frac{1}{3}$	**20** 0.4

Exercise 88B

1 $\frac{1}{6}$	**2** 0.25	**3** 0.375	**4** $\frac{1}{40}$
5 $\frac{2}{7}$	**6** 0.625	**7** $\frac{1}{5}$	**8** 0.667
9 $\frac{2}{7}$	**10** $\frac{2}{5}$	**11** $\frac{1}{2}$	**12** 0.2
13 $\frac{1}{13}$	**14** $\frac{1}{2}$	**15** 0.002	**16** $\frac{5}{7}$
17 1	**18** 0.333	**19** $\frac{1}{26}$	**20** 0.2

89 PROBABILITY: COMPLEMENTARY EVENTS

Exercise 89A

1 Not selecting the letter S, $\frac{4}{5}$

2 Picking a blue pencil, $\frac{5}{9}$

3 Picking a black card, 0.5

4 Not throwing a score of 6 or 'throwing a score of less than 6', $\frac{5}{6}$

5 Picking an even number, 0.625

6 The spinner does not come down on an R, $\frac{6}{7}$

7 Losing, 0.95

8 Not picking a heart, $\frac{3}{4}$

9 Does not come down on an N, $\frac{5}{7}$

10 Throwing an odd number, 0.5

11 Picking an odd number, 1

12 Not selecting the letter G, 0.75

13 Choosing a 2p coin, $\frac{5}{7}$

14 Not picking a blue pencil or 'picking a red or black pencil', 0.5

15 Not picking a month that starts with the letter, $\frac{3}{4}$

16 Not picking a square number, 0.286

17 Picking a card other than an ace, $\frac{12}{13}$

18 Losing, 0.96

19 Throwing a score of 3 or more, $\frac{2}{3}$

20 Not picking a red pencil or 'picking a black or blue pencil', 0.6

Exercise 89B

1 Not throwing a score of 2, $\frac{5}{6}$

2 Not picking a space or 'picking a heart, diamond or club', 0.75

3 Not selecting the letter S, 0.625

4 Losing, $\frac{39}{40}$

5 Picking a day that starts with a letter other than T or 'not picking a day starting with T', $\frac{5}{7}$

6 Picking an odd number, 0.375

7 The spinner comes down on a letter other than E, $\frac{4}{5}$

8 Picking a red pencil, 0.667

9 Not selecting the letter A, $\frac{5}{7}$

10 The spinner in the diagram does not come down on an L, $\frac{3}{5}$

11 Throwing an even number with a dice, $\frac{5}{6}$

12 Not picking a blue pencil or 'picking a red or black pencil', 0.8

13 Not picking a queen, $\frac{12}{13}$

14 Picking a number that does not contain a 7, $\frac{1}{2}$

15 Losing, 0.998

16 Choosing a 5p coin, $\frac{2}{7}$

17 Picking a number that is not a multiple of 5, 0

18 Throwing a score of 4 or less, 0.667

19 Picking a card other than a red 7, $\frac{25}{26}$

20 Not picking a black pencil or 'picking a red or blue pencil', 0.8

90 PROBABILITY: TWO COMBINED INDEPENDENT EVENTS

Exercise 90A

1

1H	2H	3H	4H	5H	6H
1D	2D	3D	4D	5D	6D
1C	2C	3C	4C	5C	6C
1S	2S	3S	4S	5S	6S

(a) $\frac{1}{24}$ (b) $\frac{1}{12}$ (c) $\frac{1}{4}$ (d) $\frac{1}{2}$

2

RH	RT
BH	BT

(a) 0.25 (b) 0.25 (c) 0.5 (d) 0.75

3

H1	H2	H3	H4	H5	H6
T1	T2	T3	T4	T5	T6

(a) $\frac{1}{12}$ (b) $\frac{1}{3}$ (c) $\frac{1}{4}$ (d) $\frac{3}{4}$

4

Hc	Hh	Ha	Hn	Hc	He
Dc	Dh	Da	Dn	Dc	De
Cc	Ch	Ca	Cn	Cc	Ce
Sc	Sh	Sa	Sn	Sc	Se

(a) 0.0417 (b) 0.0833 (c) 0.0833 (d) 0.417

5

H1	H2	H3	H4	H5
T1	T2	T3	T4	T5

(a) $\frac{1}{10}$ (b) $\frac{3}{10}$ (c) $\frac{1}{5}$ (d) $\frac{7}{10}$

6

Aa	An	Ay
La	Ln	Ly
La	Ln	Ly

(a) $\frac{1}{9}$ (b) $\frac{2}{9}$ (c) $\frac{5}{9}$ (d) $\frac{4}{9}$

7

HH	HT
TH	TT

(a) 0.25 (b) 0.5 (c) 0.75 (d) 0.25

8

1R	1B	1B
2R	2B	2B
3R	3B	3B
4R	4B	4B
5R	5B	5B
6R	6B	6B

(a) $\frac{1}{9}$ (b) $\frac{1}{9}$ (c) $\frac{1}{6}$ (d) $\frac{1}{3}$

9

11	12	12	14	15
21	22	23	24	25
31	32	33	34	35
41	42	43	44	45
51	52	53	54	55

(a) 0.04 (b) 0.12 (c) 0.16 (d) 0.8

10

11	12	13	14	15	16
21	22	23	24	25	26
31	32	33	34	35	36
41	42	43	44	45	46
51	52	53	54	55	56
61	62	63	64	65	66

(a) 0.167 (b) 0.167 (c) 0.278 (d) 0.722

Exercise 90B

1

hH	hD	hC	hS
tH	tD	tC	tS

(a) 0.25 (b) 0.125 (c) 0.25 (d) 0.75

2

Hs	He	Hl	He	Hc	Ht	He	Hd
Ts	Te	Tl	Te	Tc	Tt	Te	Td

(a) $\frac{1}{16}$ (b) $\frac{3}{16}$ (c) $\frac{3}{16}$ (d) $\frac{15}{16}$

3

HH	HD	HC	HS
DH	DD	DC	DS
CH	CD	CC	CS
SH	SD	SC	SS

(a) 0.0625 (b) 0.25 (c) 0.75 (d) 0.25

4

1R	2R	2R	4R	5R	6R
1B	2B	3B	4B	5B	6B

(a) 0.5 (b) 0.167 (c) 0.25 (d) 0.25

5

H1	H2	H3	H4	H5	H6	H7	H8
T1	T2	T3	T4	T5	T6	T7	T8

(a) $\frac{1}{16}$ (b) $\frac{1}{4}$ (c) $\frac{1}{2}$ (d) $\frac{3}{4}$

6

1R	1R	1B	1B	1B	1B
2R	2R	2B	2B	2B	2B
3R	3R	3B	3B	3B	3B
4R	4R	4B	4B	4B	4B
5R	5R	5B	5B	5B	5B
6R	6R	6B	6B	6B	6B

(a) $\frac{1}{9}$ (b) $\frac{1}{9}$ (c) $\frac{1}{3}$ (d) 0

7

11	12	13	14
21	22	23	24
31	32	33	34
41	42	43	44

(a) 0.0625 (b) 0.25 (c) 0.1975 (d) 0.75

8

Hs	Hk	Hi	Hl	Hl	Hs
Ds	Dk	Di	Dl	Dl	Ds
Cs	Ck	Ci	Cl	Cl	Cs
Ss	Sk	Si	Sl	Sl	Ss

(a) $\frac{1}{12}$ (b) $\frac{1}{6}$ (c) $\frac{1}{3}$ (d) $\frac{23}{24}$

9

HG	HG	HG	HY	HY
TG	TG	TG	TY	TY

(a) 0.3 (b) 0.5 (c) 0.2 (d) 0.8

10

EE	EX	ET	EE	EN	ET
XE	XX	XT	XE	XN	XT
TE	TX	TT	TE	TN	TT
EE	EX	ET	EE	EN	ET
NE	NX	NT	NE	NN	NT
TE	TX	TT	TE	TN	TT

(a) $\frac{1}{36}$ (b) $\frac{1}{9}$ (c) $\frac{5}{18}$ (d) $\frac{13}{18}$

R EVISION

Exercise ⊢

1 (a) $0.1 \geq$ low value > 0
(b) $0.9 <$ high value < 1
(c) 0.2–0.3
(d) high value < 1

2 (a) $\frac{3}{8}$ (b) $\frac{2}{5}$ (c) $\frac{4}{7}$ (d) $\frac{1}{2}$

3 (a) Picking a red card, $\frac{1}{2}$ (b) Losing, $\frac{122}{125}$
(c) Choosing a 5p coin, $\frac{2}{3}$
(d) Throwing a score of less than 4, $\frac{1}{2}$

4

H1	H2	H3	H4	H5
T1	T2	T3	T4	T5

(a) $\frac{1}{10}$ (b) $\frac{3}{10}$ (c) $\frac{1}{5}$ (d) 0

Exercise ⊬⊢

1 (a) Very high value < 1 (b) $\frac{1}{2}$

2

DS	DT	DA	DT	DI	DS	DT	DI	DC	DS
AS	AT	AA	AT	AI	AS	AT	AI	AC	AS
TS	TT	TA	TT	TI	TS	TT	TI	TC	TS
AS	AT	AA	AT	AI	AS	AT	AI	AC	AS

(a) $\frac{1}{4}$ (b) $\frac{11}{20}$ (c) $\frac{1}{8}$ (d) $\frac{7}{8}$

3 (a) 32 (b) $\frac{5}{32}$ (c) 0.5 (d) $\frac{1}{32}$

4 (a) $\frac{1}{18}$ (b) $\frac{2}{3}$ (c) 0.333 (d) BY and RY